G000061456

Maths Facts

Developing Problem Solving Skills
in the Daily Maths Lesson

YEAR
4

Peter Clarke

Published by Collins Educational
An imprint of HarperCollins*Publishers* Ltd
77-85 Fulham Palace Road
Hammersmith
London
W6 8JB

www.**Collins**Education.com
On-line Support for Schools and Colleges

First published 2003

10 9 8 7 6 5 4 3 2 1

© HarperCollins*Publishers* Ltd

Any educational institution that has purchased one copy of this publication may make
duplicate copies for use exclusively within that institution. Permission does not extend
to reproduction, storage in a retrieval system or transmission in any form or by any
means – electronic, mechanical, photocopying, recording or otherwise – of duplicate
copies for lending, renting or selling to any other user or institution without the prior
consent, in writing, of the publisher.

The author and publishers have done their best to ensure the accuracy of all the
information in *Maths Facts* Year 4.

Acknowledgement
A special thanks to Brian Molyneaux. Without his help, and persistence on the Internet,
this book would never have been written.

ISBN 0-00-715560-3

Publishing Manager: Melanie Hoffman
Project Editor: Ashley Lodge
Editor: Jean Rustean
Cover design by Chi Leung
Cover illustration by Tony Wilkins
Series design by Neil Adams
Illustrations by Juliet Breese, Roy Mitchell

Printed by Martins the Printers, Berwick on Tweed

Contents

Contents

Introduction

Maths Facts is a series of six books for Year 1 to Year 6. It uses topics taught in Science, Geography and History lessons to practise and consolidate the problem solving strand of the National Numeracy Strategy (NNS) *Framework for teaching mathematics from Reception to Year 6*. At the same time it develops other key mathematical concepts and skills from the numbers and the number system, calculations and measures, shape and space strands of the *Framework*.

This book contains 40 activities for a Year 4 class. Each activity consists of two parts. The first presents facts which cover the units and topics suggested in the Science, Geography and History programmes of study in the National Curriculum, and the relevant Qualifications and Curriculum Authority (QCA) schemes of work. The second part presents mathematical word problems which the children will answer by referring back to the relevant information they have been given.

Maths Facts not only develops children's mathematical ability but also reinforces the topics learnt in Science, Geography and History lessons and provides familiar and relevant contexts for the children to apply their problem solving skills.

The questions for each activity are differentiated into three levels: A, B and C. This caters for the needs of different ability groups within the class and enables each *Maths Facts* activity to be used at any time throughout the year.

Mathematical problem solving

Mathematical problem solving includes *applying mathematics* to the solution of problems arising from the environment and *reasoning* about questions that have arisen from the mathematics itself. Being able to use mathematics to analyse situations and solve real-life problems is a major reason for studying the subject. Frequent use of everyday scenarios will give meaning to the children's mathematical experiences. Children need to be able to apply the mathematics they have learned to real-life situations in their environment. They also need to be able to interpret and make meaning from their results. Teachers need to structure situations in which children investigate problems that are relevant to their daily lives and that relate to the mathematical knowledge, skills and understanding the children have most recently acquired.

Children also need to be made aware of the mathematics they are using to solve problems. Encouraging them to think about and discuss the strategies they use, and the knowledge and skills they have acquired, will assist children in developing a deeper understanding of mathematics. Discussions that arise out of mathematical problem solving can help children share experiences with each other and gain new knowledge, and will also assist them in developing their own mathematical vocabulary.

Problem solving skills

Maths Facts aims to develop in children the key skills required to tackle and solve mathematical problems. These include:

- reading and making sense of a problem

- recognising key words, relevant information and redundant information

- finding parts of a problem that can be tackled

- recognising the mathematics that can be used to help solve a problem

- deciding which number operation(s) to perform and in which order

- choosing an efficient way of calculating

- changing measurements to the same units before calculating

- getting into the habit of checking their own work to see whether the answer makes sense.

Strategies for solving mathematical problems

If children are to solve mathematical problems successfully they must be taught not only the mathematical concepts but also the strategies and procedures needed to apply these concepts. Children need to be taught to:

- look for a pattern or sequence

- experiment or act out a problem

- make a drawing or model

- make a list, table or chart

- write a number sentence

- see mathematical connections

- make and test a prediction

- make a generalisation

- establish a proof

- account for all known possibilities

- solve a simpler related problem

- work backwards.

An approach to solving mathematical problems

Children need to develop an effective and efficient method for solving mathematical problems. Page 7 provides them with a step-by-step approach to solving mathematical word problems. Photocopy and enlarge this page into a poster, and display it for all the class to see and follow during problem solving activities.

The seven steps to problem solving

Step 1 Read the problem carefully.

Step 2 What do you have to find?

Step 3 What facts are given?

Step 4 Which of the facts do you need?

Step 5 Make a plan.

Step 6 Carry out your plan to obtain your answer.

Step 7 Check your answer:
- Does it make sense?
- Put the answer back into the problem and check that it fits the information you were given.

Common pupil difficulties in problem solving

Sometimes children who are confident and capable at solving purely mathematical exercises, such as calculations, experience difficulties when it comes to solving problems. This may be due to difficulties with one or more of the following:

- reading the problem with understanding
- selecting the relevant information
- using the necessary mathematical expression
- making the required calculation correctly
- seeing relationships and using patterns
- using existing mathematical knowledge
- developing a systematic approach
- estimating the answer
- using trial-and-improvement techniques
- checking the answer
- seeing if the answer is reasonable
- recognising the connection between the answer achieved and the question asked
- being motivated
- perseverance
- confidence.

Suggestions for overcoming common pupil difficulties in problem solving

One or more of these strategies may help children who are experiencing difficulties with solving a problem.

- Present the problem orally.
- Discuss a possible approach with the children, asking appropriate questions.
- Revise any mathematical knowledge or skills needed to successfully solve the problem.
- Allow the children to work together, sharing their ideas for tackling a problem.
- Use smaller numbers.
- Use a pictorial approach if children are having difficulty with the abstract form of the problem.
- Use concrete apparatus to clarify the mathematics for the children.

- Allow the children to use appropriate resources such as a number line or hundred square to assist them with the mathematics.
- Allow the children to use a calculator.
- Use problems that are of relevance and interest to the children.

The teacher's role in problem solving lessons

- Give a choice where possible.
- Present the problem verbally, giving maximum visual support where appropriate.
- Enable children to own the problem.
- Encourage children to work together, sharing ideas for tackling a problem.
- Allow time and space for collaboration and consultation.
- Intervene, when asked, in such a way as to develop children's autonomy and independence.
- Encourage children to report the progress they are making.
- Work alongside children, setting an example yourself.
- Encourage the children to present their work to others.

The four types of word problem

All the activities in this book provide a balance between the four different types of word problem.

- The final quantity is unknown, e.g.

  - *Samantha has £1.35 and Jeanette has £1.65. How much money do they have altogether?*

  - *Matz baked 12 small cakes in each cake tin. He used two full tins. How many cakes did he bake?*

  - *Michael shared 20 grapes equally among himself and his four friends. How many did each person get?*

- The final quantity is known but not all the steps on the way, e.g.

  - *Berinda's mum baked 20 cookies. Berinda's friends came to play and ate some. How many were eaten if there were only 12 cookies left?*

  - *Sylvia needs 14 eggs. Each carton holds 6 eggs. How many cartons does she need?*

  - *Sam had 15 plants in a flower bed. He decided to throw out all the plants that were dying. He threw out 8 plants. How many plants did he keep?*

- Multi-step problems, e.g.

  - *There are 12 people on a bus. At the next stop 8 people get on and 5 get off. How many people are there on the bus now?*

  - *Steven's parents are taking Steven and his 2 sisters to the fun fair. Tickets cost £15.00 for adults and £12.50 for children. How much change do Steven's parents receive from £100?*

  - *I have enough wheels for 3 cars and there will be 2 over. How many wheels do I have?*

- Problems that involve comparisons between two or more sets, e.g.

  - *The number 59 bus has 16 people sitting downstairs and 27 people sitting upstairs. How many more people are sitting upstairs than are sitting downstairs?*

  - *I have 5 marbles, Louis has 3 and Brian has 12. Who has most? How many more does Brian have than Louis? How many more does Brian have than I do? How many more do I have than Louis?*

Maths Facts and the teaching–learning cycle

Assessment

- Guidance given on how to record pupil performance in AT1 – *Using and applying mathematics.*

Planning

- All activities provide practice and consolidation of the problem solving objectives in the NNS *Framework for teaching mathematics from Reception to Year 6.*

- Reference given to other relevant National Curriculum subjects, including National Curriculum programmes of study and QCA Primary schemes of work.

- Guidance given for planning a programme of work.

Teaching

- Consistent and easy-to-follow format for each activity.

- Guidance given on how to incorporate *Maths Facts* into the daily mathematics lesson.

Maths Facts and the daily mathematics lesson

The activities contained in *Maths Facts* are ideally suited to the daily mathematics lesson. Each activity is designed to be introduced to the whole class or group. A suggestion for a possible structure to a lesson using *Maths Facts* is given below.

- Oral work and mental calculation

  - Warm up the class by consolidating the knowledge and skills that will be used to solve the word problems.

  - Stimulate their involvement.

  - Emphasise the key vocabulary.

- Main teaching activity

  - Introduce the activity sheet to the children. Ensure that the children understand the picture and/or the vocabulary on the sheet.

  - Work through a couple of questions with the whole class, stressing possible problem solving strategies used.

  - Ask children to work in pairs on one or two of the problems.

  - Discuss these problems as a whole class.

- Pupil consolidation activities

  - Direct children's attention to the differentiated level(s) most appropriate to their needs.

  - Allow children to work individually or in pairs to solve the word problems.

  - Where needed, provide appropriate resources to assist children with the mathematics.

  - Monitor individuals, pairs or groups of children, offering support when and where necessary.

- Plenary

  - Plan an extended plenary.

  - Discuss one or two problems and possible solutions and strategies in depth with the whole class.

  - Give answers only to the remaining problems.

Curriculum information

The activities in this book provide children with an opportunity to practise and consolidate the following Year 4 problem solving objectives.

- Topic: *Making decisions*

  – Choose and use appropriate number operations and appropriate ways of calculating (mental, mental with jottings, pencil and paper) to solve problems.

- Topic: *Reasoning about numbers or shapes*

  – Explain methods and reasoning about numbers orally and in writing.

  – Solve mathematical problems or puzzles, recognise and explain patterns and relationships, generalise and predict. Suggest extensions by asking 'What if …?'

  – Make and investigate a general statement about familiar numbers or shapes by finding examples that satisfy it.

- Topic: *Problems involving 'real life', money and measures*

  – Use all four operations to solve word problems involving numbers in 'real life', money and measures (including time), using one or more steps, including converting pounds to pence and metres to centimetres and vice versa.

The National Numeracy Strategy curriculum coverage chart on page 13 shows which activity is matched to which NNS strand and topic.

The chart on pages 14–16 shows the theme for each *Maths Facts* activity and its link with the relevant National Curriculum programmes of study and QCA Primary schemes of work for Science, Geography and History.

National Numeracy Strategy curriculum coverage

Strand	Numbers and the number system			Calculations									Solving problems			Measures, shape and space		Handling data
Topic → Activity ↓	Place value, ordering and rounding (whole numbers)	Properties of numbers and number sequences	Fractions and decimals	Understanding addition and subtraction	Rapid recall of addition and subtraction facts	Mental calculation Strategies (+ and −)	Paper and pencil procedures (+ and −)	Understanding multiplication and division	Rapid recall of multiplication and division facts	Mental calculation Strategies (× and ÷)	Paper and pencil procedures (× and ÷)	Checking results of calculations	Making decisions	Reasoning about numbers or shapes	Problems involving: 'real life' (RL), money (MO), measures (ME)	Measures: Length (L), Mass (M), Capacity (C), Time (Ti), Temperature (Te), Area (A), Perimeter (P)	Shape and space	Organising and using data
1				✔	✔	✔	✔	✔	✔	✔	✔	✔	✔	✔	RL			✔
2			✔	✔	✔	✔	✔	✔	✔	✔	✔	✔	✔	✔	RL			
3				✔	✔	✔	✔	✔	✔	✔	✔	✔	✔	✔	RL			
4			✔	✔	✔	✔	✔	✔	✔	✔	✔	✔	✔	✔	RL			
5			✔	✔	✔	✔	✔	✔	✔	✔	✔	✔	✔	✔	RL			
6			✔	✔	✔	✔	✔	✔	✔	✔	✔	✔	✔	✔	RL			
7				✔	✔	✔	✔	✔	✔	✔	✔	✔	✔	✔	RL			✔
8			✔	✔	✔	✔	✔	✔	✔	✔	✔	✔	✔	✔	RL			
9	✔			✔	✔	✔	✔	✔	✔	✔	✔	✔	✔	✔	RL			
10				✔	✔	✔	✔	✔	✔	✔	✔	✔	✔	✔	RL			
11	✔			✔	✔	✔	✔	✔	✔	✔	✔	✔	✔	✔	MO			
12				✔	✔	✔	✔	✔	✔	✔	✔	✔	✔	✔	MO			
13				✔	✔	✔	✔	✔	✔	✔		✔	✔	✔	MO			
14				✔	✔	✔	✔	✔	✔	✔	✔	✔	✔	✔	MO			
15				✔	✔	✔	✔	✔	✔	✔	✔	✔	✔	✔	MO			
16				✔	✔	✔	✔	✔	✔	✔	✔	✔	✔	✔	MO			
17				✔	✔	✔	✔	✔	✔	✔	✔	✔	✔	✔	MO			✔
18				✔	✔	✔	✔	✔	✔	✔	✔	✔	✔	✔	MO			
19				✔	✔	✔	✔	✔	✔	✔	✔	✔	✔	✔	MO			
20			✔	✔	✔	✔	✔	✔	✔	✔	✔	✔	✔	✔	MO			✔
21	✔		✔	✔	✔	✔	✔	✔	✔	✔		✔	✔	✔	ME	Ti		✔
22	✔			✔	✔		✔	✔	✔			✔	✔	✔	ME	Te		✔
23				✔	✔	✔		✔	✔	✔		✔	✔	✔	ME	C/Ti/Te		
24			✔	✔	✔	✔	✔	✔	✔	✔	✔	✔	✔	✔	ME	C		
25			✔	✔	✔	✔	✔	✔	✔	✔	✔	✔	✔	✔	ME	L/M/C/Ti		
26	✔		✔	✔	✔	✔	✔	✔	✔	✔	✔	✔	✔	✔	ME	Ti/A		✔
27				✔	✔	✔	✔	✔	✔	✔	✔	✔	✔	✔	ME	L/Ti		
28				✔	✔	✔	✔	✔	✔	✔	✔	✔	✔	✔	ME	L/Ti/A		
29				✔	✔	✔	✔	✔	✔	✔	✔	✔	✔	✔	ME	L	✔	
30				✔	✔	✔	✔					✔	✔	✔	ME	L/Ti/Te		✔
31				✔	✔	✔	✔	✔	✔	✔	✔	✔	✔	✔	RL/MO/ME	Ti/A		
32				✔	✔	✔	✔	✔	✔	✔	✔	✔	✔	✔	RL/MO/ME	L/Ti/P	✔	
33	✔	✔		✔	✔	✔	✔	✔	✔	✔	✔	✔	✔	✔	RL/ME	L/M/Ti		
34	✔	✔		✔	✔	✔	✔	✔	✔	✔	✔	✔	✔	✔	RL/MO/ME	M		✔
35				✔	✔	✔	✔	✔	✔	✔	✔	✔	✔	✔	RL/MO/ME	L/Ti		
36				✔	✔	✔	✔	✔	✔	✔	✔	✔	✔	✔	RL/ME	L/M/C/Ti		
37			✔	✔	✔	✔	✔	✔	✔	✔	✔	✔	✔	✔	RL/ME	L/M/Ti		
38				✔	✔	✔	✔	✔	✔	✔	✔	✔	✔	✔	MO/ME	Ti		
39			✔	✔	✔	✔	✔	✔	✔	✔	✔	✔	✔	✔	RL/MO/ME	M/C		✔
40			✔	✔	✔	✔	✔	✔	✔	✔	✔	✔	✔	✔	RL/MO/ME	L/Ti		

Links with National Curriculum programmes of study and QCA Primary schemes of work

Curriculum subject	Key Stage 2 National Curriculum programme of study	QCA Primary scheme of work	*Maths Facts* theme	Activity
Science	Sc2 Life processes and living things 1 Life processes 2 Humans and other animals Breadth of study: 1 / 2	4A. Moving and growing	What do you eat?	1
			Bones and things	2
			How long do they live?	21
	Sc2 Life processes and living things 1 Life processes 4 Variation and classification 5 Living things in their environment Breadth of study: 1 / 2	4B Habitats	Pond life	31
			Woodlands	32
			The rabbit warren	33
	Sc3 Materials and their properties 1 Grouping and classifying materials 2 Changing materials Breadth of study: 1 / 2	4C Keeping warm	The cost of keeping warm	11
			Thermometer readings	22
			Thermal insulators	23
	Sc3 Materials and their properties 1 Grouping and classifying materials 2 Changing materials 3 Separating mixtures of materials Breadth of study: 1 / 2	4D Solids, liquids and how they can be separated	Sandy's Fish and Chip Shop	12
			The Bubbly Drinks Company	24
			The restaurant kitchen	25
	Sc3 Materials and their properties 1 Grouping and classifying materials Sc4 Physical processes 2 Forces and motion Breadth of study: 1 / 2	4E Friction	Parachutes	26
			Tobogganing	27
	Sc3 Materials and their properties 1 Grouping and classifying materials Sc4 Physical processes 1 Electricity Breadth of study: 1 / 2	4F Circuits and conductors	The Better Electrics' Sale	13
			Sparky the electrician	14
			The electrician's shop	15
Geography	Knowledge, skills and understanding 3 Knowledge and understanding of places 4 Knowledge and understanding of patterns and processes 5 Knowledge and understanding of environmental change and sustainable development Breadth of study: 6 / 7	8 Improving the environment 24 Passport to the world 25 Geography and numbers	Improving Peddler's Park Junior School	16
			Recycling	34
	Knowledge, skills and understanding 3 Knowledge and understanding of places 4 Knowledge and understanding of patterns and processes 5 Knowledge and understanding of environmental change and sustainable development Breadth of study: 6 / 7	9 Village settlers 24 Passport to the world 25 Geography and numbers	Mr. and Mrs. Herne's Farm	28
			The village of Wellford	35
	Knowledge, skills and understanding 3 Knowledge and understanding of places 4 Knowledge and understanding of patterns and processes 5 Knowledge and understanding of environmental change and sustainable development Breadth of study: 6 / 7	10 A village in India 24 Passport to the world 25 Geography and numbers	The village of Chembakolli	29
			Padmi, a woman from Chembakolli	36

Curriculum subject	Key Stage 2 National Curriculum programme of study	QCA Primary scheme of work	*Maths Facts* theme	Activity
Geography *(continued)*	Knowledge, skills and understanding 3 Knowledge and understanding of places 4 Knowledge and understanding of patterns and processes Breadth of study: 6 / 7	16 What's in the news? 24 Passport to the world 25 Geography and numbers	The Six o'clock News	3
			Briton in Spacewalk	37
	Knowledge, skills and understanding 3 Knowledge and understanding of places 4 Knowledge and understanding of patterns and processes Breadth of study: 6 / 7	18 Connecting ourselves to the world 24 Passport to the world 25 Geography and numbers	Quick-link Internet Company	17
			London, England and Sabah, Malaysia	30
	Knowledge, skills and understanding 4 Knowledge and understanding of patterns and processes Breadth of study: 6 / 7	19 How and where do we spend our time? 25 Geography and numbers	What we did last week	18
			Elroy's week	38
	Knowledge, skills and understanding 3 Knowledge and understanding of places 4 Knowledge and understanding of patterns and processes 5 Knowledge and understanding of environmental change and sustainable development Breadth of study: 6 / 7	21 How can we improve the area we can see from our window? 25 Geography and numbers	Improving Moss Vale Primary	19
History	Knowledge, skills and understanding 1 Chronological understanding 2 Knowledge and understanding of events, people and changes in the past Breadth of study: 8a / 9	6A Why have people invaded and settled in Britain in the past? A Roman case study	The Roman navy and army	4
	Knowledge, skills and understanding 1 Chronological understanding 2 Knowledge and understanding of events, people and changes in the past Breadth of study: 8a / 9	6B Why have people invaded and settled in Britain in the past? An Anglo-Saxon case study	The Saxons	5
	Knowledge, skills and understanding 1 Chronological understanding 2 Knowledge and understanding of events, people and changes in the past Breadth of study: 8a / 9	6C Why have people invaded and settled in Britain in the past? A Viking case study	The Vikings	6
	Knowledge, skills and understanding 1 Chronological understanding 2 Knowledge and understanding of events, people and changes in the past Breadth of study: 10	7 Why did Henry VIII marry six times?	Henry VIII	7
	Knowledge, skills and understanding 1 Chronological understanding 2 Knowledge and understanding of events, people and changes in the past Breadth of study: 10	8 What were the differences between the lives of rich and poor people in Tudor times?	Rich and poor Tudors	8
	Knowledge, skills and understanding 1 Chronological understanding 2 Knowledge and understanding of events, people and changes in the past Breadth of study: 11b	9 What was it like for children in the Second World War?	Pay and costs during World War II	20
			Rationing in World War II	39

Curriculum subject	Key Stage 2 National Curriculum programme of study	QCA Primary scheme of work	*Maths Facts* theme	Activity
History *(continued)*	Knowledge, skills and understanding 1 Chronological understanding 2 Knowledge and understanding of events, people and changes in the past Breadth of study: 13	10 What can we find out about ancient Egypt from what has survived?	Tutankhamun's Tomb	9
			Ancient Egypt	10
	Knowledge, skills and understanding 1 Chronological understanding 2 Knowledge and understanding of events, people and changes in the past Breadth of study: 11b	18 What was it like to live in the past?	Brian's life	40

General guidance for Levels A, B and C in *Maths Facts* Year 4

Level A

Children should have been introduced to the following objectives:

- Read and write whole numbers to at least 10 000 in figures and words, and know what each digit represents.
- Understand decimal notation for tenths and hundredths, and use it in context.
- Consolidate knowing by heart addition and subtraction facts for all numbers to 20.
- Derive quickly:
  - all number pairs that total 100;
  - all pairs of multiples of 50 with a total of 1000.
- Know by heart multiplication facts for 2, 3, 4, 5 and 10 times-tables.
- Derive quickly:
  - division facts corresponding to 2, 3, 4, 5 and 10 times-tables;
  - doubles of all whole numbers to 50;
  - doubles of multiples of 10 to 500;
  - doubles of multiples of 100 to 5000;
  - and all the corresponding halves.

If children experience difficulty with questions at this level provide them with:
- 1–100 number square   • multiplication square

Level B

Children should have been introduced to the following objectives:

Level A objectives and:

- Use known number facts and place value to add or subtract mentally, including any pair of two-digit whole numbers.
- Use informal pencil and paper methods to support, record or explain additions/subtractions.
- Begin to know multiplication facts for 6, 7, 8 and 9 times-tables.
- Use known number facts and place value to multiply and divide integers, including by 10 and then 100 (whole-number answers).

If children experience difficulty with questions at this level provide them with:
- 1–100 number square   • multiplication square   • calculator

Level C

Children should have been introduced to the following objectives:

Level A and B objectives and:

- Develop and refine written methods for:
  - column addition and subtraction of two whole numbers less than 1000;
  - addition of more than two such numbers;
  - money calculations.
- Approximate first. Use informal pencil and paper methods to support, record or explain multiplications and divisions.
- Develop and refine written methods for TU × U, TU ÷ U.

If children experience difficulty with questions at this level provide them with:

- 1–100 number square
- multiplication square
- calculator

Planning a programme of work for *Maths Facts*

The *Maths Facts* Programme chart on page 18 may be used in conjunction with your long- and medium-term plans to develop a *Maths Facts* programme of work throughout the year. By following the topics allocated using the NNS *Framework for teaching mathematics from Reception to Year 6* or similar scheme of work you will ensure that the children not only have an opportunity to practise and consolidate the topic and specific objectives for a particular week but also, where appropriate, link this with other National Curriculum subjects.

Maths Facts and assessment

Maths Facts activities may be used with the whole class or with groups of children as an assessment activity. Linked to the topic that is being studied at present, *Maths Facts* will provide you with an indication of how well the children have understood the objectives being covered as well as their problem solving skills.

The assessment and record-keeping format on page 19 can be used to assess and level individual children in Attainment Target 1: *Using and applying mathematics*. By observing individual children while they undertake a *Maths Facts* activity, discussing their work with them and subsequently marking their work, you will be able to gain a good understanding of their problem solving, communicating and reasoning skills. Your judgements about an individual child's abilities can then be entered onto the assessment and record-keeping format and this will provide you with an Attainment Target 1 Level. It is envisaged that one copy of the assessment and record-keeping format would be used for your entire class.

Maths Facts Programme

Year: _____   Class: _____

Teacher: _____

Week	Mathematics topic	Other National Curriculum subject and topic	*Maths Facts* activity
AUTUMN 1			
2			
3			
4			
5			
6			
7			
8			
9			
10			
11			
12			
SPRING 1			
2			
3			
4			
5			
6			
7			
8			
9			
10			
11			
12			
SUMMER 1			
2			
3			
4			
5			
6			
7			
8			
9			
10			
11			
12			

Maths Facts (Y4) © HarperCollins*Publishers* Ltd 2003

Attainment Target 1: *Using and applying mathematics*
Assessment and record-keeping format

Year: _____   Class: _____

Teacher: _____

LEVEL 2

Problem solving
- Select and use material in some classroom activities
- Select and use mathematics for some classroom activities
- Begin to develop own strategies for solving a problem
- Begin to understand ways of working through a problem

Communicating
- Discuss work using mathematical language
- Respond to and ask mathematical questions
- Begin to represent work using symbols and simple diagrams
- Explain why an answer is correct

Reasoning
- Ask questions such as: 'What would happen if … ?' 'Why?'
- Begin to develop simple strategies

LEVEL 3

Problem solving
- Develop different mathematical approaches to a problem
- Look for ways to overcome difficulties
- Begin to make decisions and realise that results may vary according to the 'rule' used
- Begin to organise work
- Check results

Communicating
- Discuss mathematical work
- Begin to explain thinking
- Use and interpret mathematical symbols and diagrams

Reasoning
- Understand a general statement
- Investigate general statements and predictions by finding and trying out examples

LEVEL 4

Problem solving
- Develop own strategies for solving problems
- Use own strategies for working within mathematics
- Use own strategies for applying mathematics to practical contexts

Communicating
- Present information and results in a clear and organised way

Reasoning
- Search for solutions by trying out own ideas

GENERAL COMMENTS

Activity 1

Name _____

Date _____

What do you eat?

This table shows how many calories are in different foods.

Food	Average portion	Calories
Apple	1	170
Banana	1	110
Beef	200 g steak	388
Bread (wholemeal)	1 slice	80
Butter	for 1 slice	110
Cheese (cheddar)	100 g	410
Chips	170 g	270
Corn flakes	1 bowl	100
Egg (boiled)	1	90
Milk	cup	110
Orange	1	60
Sardines (tinned)	4 fish	240
Sausages	2	400
Sugar	1 teaspoon	25
Tomato	1	12

This table shows how many calories are needed every day.

Age	Calories
0 – 1	800
1 – 2	1200
2 – 3	1400
3 – 5	1600
5 – 7	1800
7 – 9	2100
9 – 12	2400
12 – 15	2600
15 – 18	2700

> Show any working on the back of this sheet.

A 1 A child of 0 – 1 years needs 800 calories a day. Between what ages does a child need twice this number of calories?

2 Toni has one sausage and a portion of chips for tea. How many calories is this?

3 Children between the ages of 9 and 12 need 2400 calories a day. Which age group needs half this number of calories?

B 1 How many calories are there in three slices of wholemeal bread and butter?

2 Every morning Sally has a boiled egg and a slice of toast with butter for breakfast. How many calories is this?

3 Barbara is making fruit salad. She uses 2 oranges, 2 apples, 2 bananas and 2 teaspoons of sugar. How many calories does it contain?

4 Tina has one sardine on buttered toast for tea. How many calories does she eat?

C 1 Leroy has 100 g of beef steak and a portion of chips for lunch. How many calories is this?

2 Mrs. Warren is making sandwiches. She uses 2 tomatoes, 100 g of cheese and 4 slices of buttered wholemeal bread. How many calories is this altogether?

3 Sami is 10 years old. At breakfast she eats 540 calories, at lunch she eats 835 calories, after school she has a snack of 255 calories and for tea she has 705 calories. Does she eat more or less calories than she needs? How many more or less?

Bones and things

Show any working on the back of this sheet.

A 1 Your skull has 29 bones. 8 of these form a helmet around the brain called the cranium. How many bones in your skull are not part of the cranium?

2 Your ribs form a cage to protect your heart and lungs. Most people have 12 pairs of ribs. How many ribs is this?

3 1 person in 20 has an extra rib. In a group of 100 people, how many of them will have an extra rib?

B 1 A newborn baby has about 300 bones. By the time it has become an adult, some of the bones have joined together and it has only 206 bones. How many fewer bones does an adult have than a baby?

2 An adult has 206 bones. Roughly half of these are in the hands and feet. Approximately how many bones are in the hands and feet?

3 About $\frac{1}{5}$ of your body weight is bone. If you weigh 30 kg, how much do your bones weigh?

4 Each year, the hair on your head grows 12 cm, while your fingernails grow 3·5 cm. How much more each year does your hair grow than your fingernails?

C 1 Each hair of your head lives for roughly 3 years. Your eyelashes live for roughly 150 days. If there are 365 days in a year, how much longer does the hair on your head live for?

2 Adults have between 4·5 and 7 litres of blood in their body. Of this, $\frac{11}{20}$ is a colourless fluid called plasma. The rest of it is made of red blood cells. What fraction of the blood is red blood cells?

3 About $\frac{2}{5}$ of the weight of your body is muscle. If you weigh 25 kg, how much do your muscles weigh?

Activity 3

Problems involving 'real life'
Geography: 16. What's in the news?

Name _____

Date _____

The Six o'clock News

Show any working on the back of this sheet.

A 1 There has been an earthquake in Italy and a school has collapsed. 24 children have been rescued but it is feared that another 21 children are still trapped. How many children is this altogether?

2 There were 56 children and 6 adults in the school when the earthquake happened. How many people were in the school?

3 The earthquake started at 11:40 am and ended at 1:00 pm. How long did the earthquake last?

B 1 The government has admitted that half the Royal Navy's warships are out of action due to strikes. 18 warships are out of action. How many warships are there altogether in the navy?

2 The government had previously said that there would always be 26 warships ready for action. If there are only 18 in action, by how many are they short?

3 The government has said that the new army helicopters will not be ready until 2012, 12 years after they were due in service. When were they due in service?

4 3 regiments, each with 16 helicopters, are to be a key part of the army. How many helicopters will they have in total?

C 1 A study just released says that about 1100 species of birds and mammals will become extinct in the next 20 years. Roughly, how many species will disappear each year?

2 In the last 400 years, 185 species of birds and mammals disappeared. In the next 20 years 1100 species will disappear. How many more will disappear in the next 20 years than disappeared in the last 400?

3 The study says that 10 000 species of plants and 1100 species of birds and mammals will disappear in the next 20 years. How many species is this altogether?

Activity 4

Problems involving 'real life'
History: 6A. Why have people invaded and settled in Britain in the past? A Roman case study

Name _____

Date _____

The Roman navy and army

Show any working on the back of this sheet.

A 1 A Roman warship had about 300 men rowing and carried 120 men on deck to fight. How many men did each warship hold altogether?

2 Roman warships were rowed and could travel up to 19 km each hour. Roman cargo ships had sails and could travel up to 7 km each hour. How much further could warships travel in an hour than cargo ships?

3 Roman soldiers earned 300 denarii a year. They spent about $\frac{1}{3}$ of this on food. How much did they spend on food a year?

B 1 Each month during training Roman soldiers had to go on 3 marches of 30 km each. How far did they march in a month?

2 How long did it take Roman soldiers to march 30 km if they marched 7·5 km each hour?

3 Romans built roads so that their army could move from place to place quickly. Minor Roman roads were 3·5 m wide and major roads were 7·7 m wide. How much wider were the major roads?

4 The Roman government built guesthouses on the roads every 15 miles. If two towns were 60 miles apart, how many guesthouses were between them?

C 1 The Roman army was divided into legions of 4200 men each. If mutiny was suspected, 1 out of every 10 men was executed. How many men were executed in a legion if mutiny was suspected?

2 Each legion was divided into groups called maniples. Each maniple consisted of 120 men. If there were 4200 men in a legion, how many maniples were there in each legion?

3 Each maniple consisted of 120 men. These were divided into groups of 8 men who shared a tent. How many tents were needed for each maniple?

Activity 5

Problems involving 'real life'
History: 6B. Why have people invaded and settled in Britain in the past? An Anglo-Saxon case study

Name _____

Date _____

The Saxons

Show any working on the back of this sheet.

A

1 In Saxon times, most people did not live long. By the time a person was 13 they had lived half their life. How long did most people live for?

2 Saxon horses cost $\frac{1}{2}$ a pound of silver each. How many horses could you buy with 6 pounds of silver?

3 Saxon ploughs were called carrucas. They needed 4 oxen to pull them. If a village had 6 ploughs, how many oxen did they need to pull all their ploughs at the same time?

B

1 Saxon ploughs needed 4 oxen to pull them. Oxen cost 30 pieces of silver. How many pieces of silver did it cost to buy the oxen needed to pull one plough?

2 In Saxon times, pigs cost 10p each and sheep cost 4p each. How much did it cost to buy 8 pigs and 6 sheep?

3 If you killed a village Lord in Saxon times you had to pay his family 1200 shillings. If you killed a landowner you had to pay 200 shillings. How much more did you have to pay if you killed a village Lord than a landowner?

4 In Saxon times, people who rented land had to work 2 days each week for the landlord for 48 weeks of the year, and 3 days a week for 4 weeks of the year during harvest. How many days did they work for the landlord in a year?

C

1 In Saxon times, land was divided into units called strips. If the strips were 2000 m² in area and 5 strips make a larger unit called a hectare, how many square metres are there in a hectare?

2 In Saxon times, land was divided into strips. Each strip was $\frac{1}{5}$ of a hectare in size. If a freeman had 120 strips of land, how many hectares did he have?

3 When the Saxons invaded England there were 2500 villa farms left by the Romans. 50 years later there were only 850 left. How many villa farms did the Saxons destroy during this time?

Activity 6

Problems involving 'real life'
History: 6C. Why have people invaded and settled in Britain in the past? A Viking case study

Name _____

Date _____

The Vikings

Show any working on the back of this sheet.

A **1** A Viking ship had a crew of 35 men. How many crew were needed for 2 ships?

2 Viking ships were about 24 metres long with a mast of half this length. How long were the masts?

3 In Viking times, women got up at about 6:00 am and went to bed 17 hours later. At what time did they go to bed?

B **1** The Viking alphabet was called the Runic Alphabet. It originally had 24 letters, but by about AD 900 there were only 16 letters. By how many letters was the alphabet reduced?

2 Viking spears were about 3 m long. Viking swords were about 80 cm long. How much longer were Vikings spears than swords?

3 A Viking ship could travel 193 km in a day. How many kilometres could it travel in 2 days?

4 A Viking merchant ship with a crew of 6 men could travel 2400 km between Yorvik, in England, and Norway in about 2 weeks. How far did the ship travel there and back?

C **1** Viking ships had square sails. If the area of a sail was 81 m^2, what were its dimensions?

2 $\frac{1}{2}$ the meat that Vikings ate came from cows, $\frac{3}{10}$ came from sheep and the rest from pigs. What fraction of the meat that Vikings ate came from pigs?

3 A Viking merchant ship with a crew of 6 men and a cargo of 5 tonnes could travel 1200 km in a week. A Viking warship with a crew of 35 men and a cargo 4 times the size of a merchant ship could travel 1350 km in a week. How much further could a warship travel in a week?

Activity 7

Problems involving 'real life'
History: 7. Why did Henry VIII marry six times?

Name _____

Date _____

Henry VIII

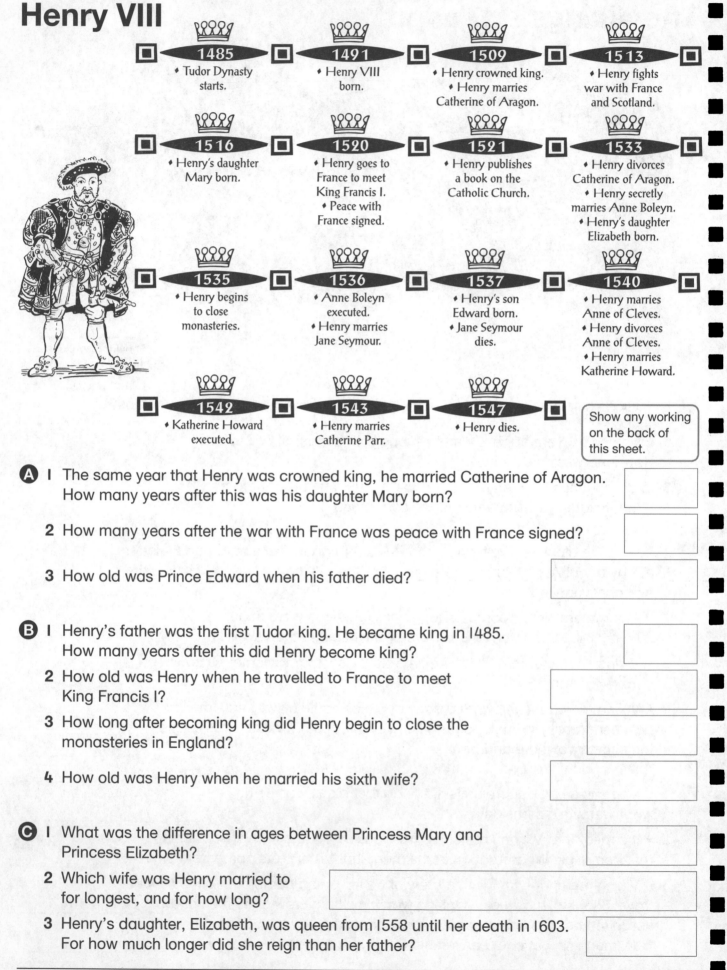

1485
* Tudor Dynasty starts.

1491
* Henry VIII born.

1509
* Henry crowned king.
* Henry marries Catherine of Aragon.

1513
* Henry fights war with France and Scotland.

1516
* Henry's daughter Mary born.

1520
* Henry goes to France to meet King Francis I.
* Peace with France signed.

1521
* Henry publishes a book on the Catholic Church.

1533
* Henry divorces Catherine of Aragon.
* Henry secretly marries Anne Boleyn.
* Henry's daughter Elizabeth born.

1535
* Henry begins to close monasteries.

1536
* Anne Boleyn executed.
* Henry marries Jane Seymour.

1537
* Henry's son Edward born.
* Jane Seymour dies.

1540
* Henry marries Anne of Cleves.
* Henry divorces Anne of Cleves.
* Henry marries Katherine Howard.

1542
* Katherine Howard executed.

1543
* Henry marries Catherine Parr.

1547
* Henry dies.

Show any working on the back of this sheet.

A 1 The same year that Henry was crowned king, he married Catherine of Aragon. How many years after this was his daughter Mary born?

2 How many years after the war with France was peace with France signed?

3 How old was Prince Edward when his father died?

B 1 Henry's father was the first Tudor king. He became king in 1485. How many years after this did Henry become king?

2 How old was Henry when he travelled to France to meet King Francis I?

3 How long after becoming king did Henry begin to close the monasteries in England?

4 How old was Henry when he married his sixth wife?

C 1 What was the difference in ages between Princess Mary and Princess Elizabeth?

2 Which wife was Henry married to for longest, and for how long?

3 Henry's daughter, Elizabeth, was queen from 1558 until her death in 1603. For how much longer did she reign than her father?

Activity 8

Problems involving 'real life'
History: 8. What were the differences between the lives of poor and rich people in Tudor times?

Name _____

Date _____

Rich and poor Tudors

Show any working on the back of this sheet.

A
1. In Tudor times, only 1 in 10 people reached the age of 40. Queen Elizabeth I lived 29 years longer than this. How long did she live for?

2. 800 people attended Henry VIII's court. 1500 attended Elizabeth I's court. How many more people attended Elizabeth's court?

3. When Elizabeth I travelled, she took 400 horse-drawn carts of luggage with her. They travelled about 5 kilometres each hour. How long did they take to travel 20 kilometres?

B
1. In summer, rich children started school at 6:00 am. In winter, they started an hour later. School finished at 5:30 pm throughout the year. For how many hours were children at school each day in winter?

2. Hampton Court Palace was built in Tudor times. It had about 1000 rooms. 280 of these were bedrooms. How many other rooms were there?

3. In Tudor times, one quarter of the population was poor. Out of 100 people how many people were poor?

4. In Tudor times, 45 people were hanged each month in England for committing a crime. How many people were hanged each year?

C
1. Once, during a royal banquet, Henry VIII and his guests ate 11400 cows and 2200 sheep. How many cows and sheep is this altogether?

2. In Tudor times the Church gave pensions of $2\frac{1}{2}$p each week to each poor person. If there were 100 poor people in a village, how much money did the Church give out in that village each week?

3. In 1528 about $\frac{1}{6}$ of the population died of the plague. In a village of 300 people, how many people died?

Activity 9

Problems involving 'real life'
History: 10. What can we find out
about Ancient Egypt from what
has survived?

Name _____

Date _____

Tutankhamun's Tomb

Howard Carter and Lord Caernarvon discovered the tomb of the
Egyptian pharaoh Tutankhamun.

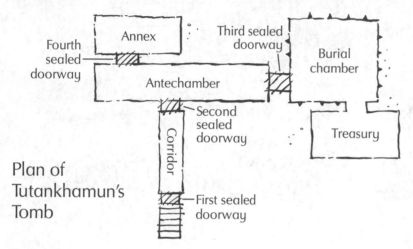

Plan of
Tutankhamun's
Tomb

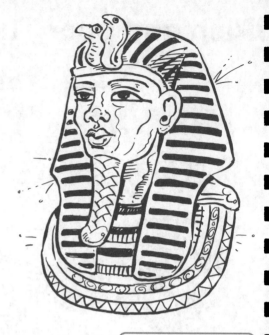

Show any working on
the back of this sheet.

A 1 Howard Carter arrived in Egypt in 1900. He discovered the tomb
of Tutankhamun in 1922. How many years after arriving in Egypt did he
discover the tomb?

2 Howard Carter found the tomb of Tutankhamun on 4th November 1922.
He immediately informed Lord Caernarvon who arrived 19 days later.
What was the date that Lord Caernarvon
arrived in Egypt?

3 At the bottom of the steps leading to the tomb was a corridor 8 m long
and 2 m wide. What was the floor area of the corridor?

B 1 In Tutankhamun's tomb about 600 objects were found in one room and
2000 in another. How many objects were found in the two rooms altogether?

2 60 figures of Tutankhamun, gods and animals were found in the tomb, as well
as 413 wooden figures called shabtis. How many figures is this altogether?

3 413 shabtis figures were found in the tomb. 365 of them represented workmen,
one for each day of the year, the remainder were overseers. How many were
overseers?

4 About 500 objects were found in the Treasury. Of these 35 were model boats.
How many were not?

C 1 Fine shawls were found in the tomb. It is estimated that it took one person
9 months, working 11 hours a day, to make each
shawl. Approximately, how many hours is this?

2 Howard Carter first visited Egypt in September 1891, aged 17 years.
He discovered Tutankhamun's tomb in 1922. How old was he when
he discovered the tomb?

3 Tutankhamun died in 1327 BC, aged 19. In which year was he born?

Maths Facts (Y4) © HarperCollins*Publishers* Ltd 2003

Activity 10

Problems involving 'real life'

History: 10. What can we find out about Ancient Egypt from what has survived?

Name _____

Date _____

Ancient Egypt

Show any working on the back of this sheet.

A 1 The Egyptian army was made up of many divisions, each with 5000 men in it. Of these 5000, 4000 were foot soldiers and the rest were charioteers. How many charioteers were there in each division?

2 1 in 10 able men were called up to join the army. Out of 200 able men, how many were called up to join the army?

3 In Ancient Egypt a typical worker's house had 3 rooms, a yard where the kitchen was and 2 cellars for storage. In a district of 1200 houses, how many cellars were there?

B 1 Ancient Egypt did not have a 7 day week. They worked for 8 days and then had 2 days holiday. How many days did they work in 60 days?

2 The base of the Great Pyramid was originally a square, 230 m long and 230 m wide. What was the perimeter of the base?

3 In Ancient Egypt the year was divided into 3 equal seasons. The Wet Season, followed by the Growing Season and then the Dry Season. If the Wet Season started in July, when did the Dry Season start?

4 Each division of the Ancient Egyptian army had 5000 men in it. They were normally housed in barracks with 10 men to each room. How many rooms were needed to house one division?

C 1 Barges for carrying things on the Nile River were too big to be rowed. They were towed by up to 27 smaller boats, each manned by 30 oarsmen. How many oarsmen were needed for 27 boats?

2 The River Nile is 6690 km long. For the last 160 km it flows through the Nile Delta. How far does it flow before it reaches the Delta?

3 Each division of the Egyptian Army had 4000 foot soldiers. These were divided into companies of 200 men. How many companies were the 4000 men divided into?

The cost of keeping warm

Sweater £25

Gas heater £77

Woollen socks £4

Hot water bottle £9

Double glazed window £450

Roll of loft insulation £8

Electric heater £32

Thermal underwear £43

Electric blanket £17

£1000

Show any working on the back of this sheet.

A 1 Larry is going hiking in winter and needs a set of thermal underwear, a pair of woollen socks and a sweater. How much does this cost him?

2 Is it cheaper for Mr. and Mrs. Howard to buy a hot water bottle each or one electric blanket?

3 The gas heater costs 4p an hour to run. How much does it cost to have it on for 8 hours?

B 1 What is the total cost of 4 electric blankets?

2 The electric heater costs 12p an hour to run and the gas heater costs 4p an hour. How much more does it cost to run the electric heater for 20 hours than the gas heater?

3 Mr. Smith has spent £231 on 3 gas heaters and £96 on 12 rolls of loft insulation. How much does this cost him altogether?

4 It costs Mr. George £843 a year to heat his house. If he put in loft insulation it would cost him £90 a year less. What would his heating bill be for a year if he insulated his loft?

C 1 Better Glaze is offering a special promotion. They will replace 3 of your windows with double glazing for the cost of only 2 windows. If Mr. Janson wants 6 windows replaced, how much will this cost him?

2 Mr. Mulouf is insulating his loft and needs 27 rolls of loft insulation. How much does this cost him?

3 How many rolls of loft insulation can you buy for £90?

Activity 12

Problems involving money
Science: 4D. Solids, liquids and
how they can be separated

Name _____

Date _____

Sandy's Fish and Chip Shop

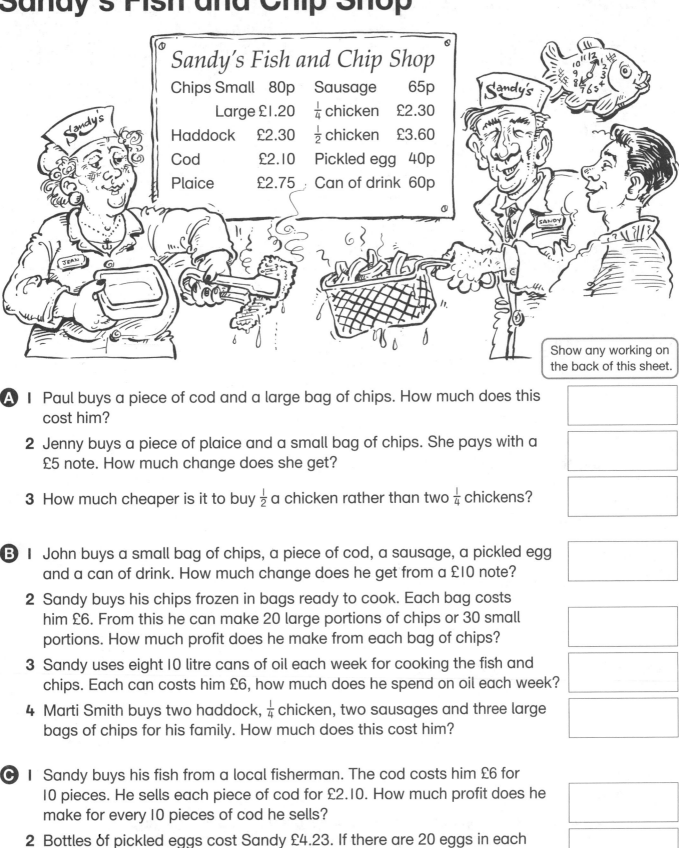

Sandy's Fish and Chip Shop

Chips Small	80p	Sausage	65p
Large	£1.20	$\frac{1}{4}$ chicken	£2.30
Haddock	£2.30	$\frac{1}{2}$ chicken	£3.60
Cod	£2.10	Pickled egg	40p
Plaice	£2.75	Can of drink	60p

Show any working on
the back of this sheet.

A 1 Paul buys a piece of cod and a large bag of chips. How much does this cost him?

2 Jenny buys a piece of plaice and a small bag of chips. She pays with a £5 note. How much change does she get?

3 How much cheaper is it to buy $\frac{1}{2}$ a chicken rather than two $\frac{1}{4}$ chickens?

B 1 John buys a small bag of chips, a piece of cod, a sausage, a pickled egg and a can of drink. How much change does he get from a £10 note?

2 Sandy buys his chips frozen in bags ready to cook. Each bag costs him £6. From this he can make 20 large portions of chips or 30 small portions. How much profit does he make from each bag of chips?

3 Sandy uses eight 10 litre cans of oil each week for cooking the fish and chips. Each can costs him £6, how much does he spend on oil each week?

4 Marti Smith buys two haddock, $\frac{1}{4}$ chicken, two sausages and three large bags of chips for his family. How much does this cost him?

C 1 Sandy buys his fish from a local fisherman. The cod costs him £6 for 10 pieces. He sells each piece of cod for £2.10. How much profit does he make for every 10 pieces of cod he sells?

2 Bottles of pickled eggs cost Sandy £4.23. If there are 20 eggs in each bottle, how much profit does he make?

3 Sandy is open 6 days a week. Last week he took £45.30 on Monday, £63.45 on Tuesday, £81.95 on Thursday, £129.05 on Friday, £163.65 on Saturday and £92.40 on Sunday. How much did he make last week?

The Better Electrics' Sale

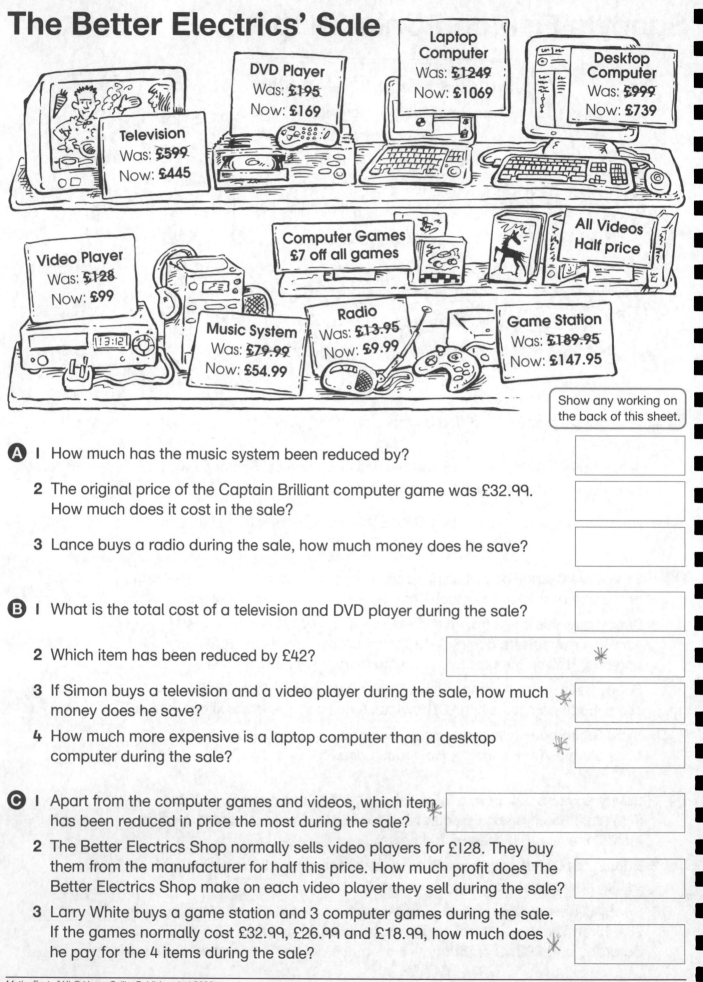

Laptop Computer
Was: £1249
Now: £1069

Desktop Computer
Was: £999
Now: £739

DVD Player
Was: £195
Now: £169

Television
Was: £599
Now: £445

Video Player
Was: £128
Now: £99

Computer Games
£7 off all games

All Videos Half price

Music System
Was: £79.99
Now: £54.99

Radio
Was: £13.95
Now: £9.99

Game Station
Was: £189.95
Now: £147.95

> Show any working on the back of this sheet.

A 1 How much has the music system been reduced by?

2 The original price of the Captain Brilliant computer game was £32.99. How much does it cost in the sale?

3 Lance buys a radio during the sale, how much money does he save?

B 1 What is the total cost of a television and DVD player during the sale?

2 Which item has been reduced by £42?

3 If Simon buys a television and a video player during the sale, how much money does he save?

4 How much more expensive is a laptop computer than a desktop computer during the sale?

C 1 Apart from the computer games and videos, which item has been reduced in price the most during the sale?

2 The Better Electrics Shop normally sells video players for £128. They buy them from the manufacturer for half this price. How much profit does The Better Electrics Shop make on each video player they sell during the sale?

3 Larry White buys a game station and 3 computer games during the sale. If the games normally cost £32.99, £26.99 and £18.99, how much does he pay for the 4 items during the sale?

Activity 14

Problems involving money
Science: 4F. Circuits and
conductors

Name _____

Date _____

Sparky the electrician

Show any working on
the back of this sheet.

A 1 Sparky installs a burglar alarm for Mrs. Mangles. It takes him 8 hours.
He charges £20 to travel to her house and £30 for each hour of work.
How much does this work cost her?

2 Mrs. Patience asks Sparky to install a ventilation fan in her bathroom.
He charges her £35 for the fan, £2 for the switch, 50p for the wire and
£110 for his labour. How much does Mrs. Patience have to pay?

3 Sparky charges £260 a day for his labour. He charges twice this amount
for working at the weekend. How much does he charge for a day at
the weekend?

B 1 Sparky is rewiring Mrs. Costello's house. He needs to replace 10 light
switches. If each switch costs £2.45, how much do they cost altogether?

2 Sparky buys 15 plug sockets for Mrs. Costello's house. They each
cost £3. What is the total cost of these?

3 Sparky buys 50 metres of 1·5 mm wire at 50p a metre and 50 metres of
2·5 mm wire at £1.20 a metre. How much does the wire cost?

4 Sparky charges £260 a day. It took him 5 days to rewire Mrs. Costello's
house. How much does he charge Mrs. Costello for his work?

C 1 Sparky fits an outside security light for Mr. Jones. He charges Mr. Jones
£150 altogether. If the light costs him £29.99, the switch £2.45 and the
wire 50p, how much does he charge for his work?

2 Sparky charges £260 a day for his labour. He charges twice this amount
for working at the weekend. How much would he earn if he worked
Friday, Saturday and Sunday on a job?

3 Sparky keeps a supply of switches, plugs, lights and wire at his home.
He has £342 worth of switches, £420 worth of plugs, £183 worth of lights
and £197 worth of wire. How much is this altogether?

The electrician's shop

Price list

1·5 mm wire 60p a metre

2·5 mm wire £1.50 a metre

6·5 mm wire £4.50 a metre

Insulating tape £1.80 per roll

Sockets £3

Plugs £1.55

Switches £2.45

Junction boxes £2.30

Show any working on the back of this sheet.

A 1 What is the difference in price of 1·5 mm wire and 6·5 mm wire?

2 William buys 3 metres of 2·5 mm wire and pays with a £5 note. How much change does he get?

3 Jo buys 2 metres of 1·5 mm wire, a plug and a switch, and also a light which costs £23. How much does this cost him altogether?

B 1 Frank needs 7 metres of 2·5 mm wire for his new washing machine. How much does this cost him?

2 One socket costs £3. If you buy 50 or more, the price of all of them is reduced by 40p per socket. How much does it cost to buy 50 sockets?

3 Sam buys 5 rolls of insulating tape and pays with a £10 note, how much change does he get?

4 Although anyone can buy things at the electrician's shop, electricians themselves get a discount. A fan that costs £32.99 can be bought by an electrician for £29.69. How much of a saving is this for the electrician?

C 1 The electrical supplier sells 100 metre rolls of 2·5 mm wire for £128. How much cheaper is this than buying the wire at £1.50 a metre?

2 Glen is redecorating and buys 3 sockets, 2 junction boxes, a roll of insulating tape and 12 metres of 2·5 mm wire. How much does he pay?

3 One switch costs £2.45. If you buy 100 or more the price of all of them is reduced to £2.08 per switch. How much do 150 cost?

Activity 16

Problems involving money
Geography: 8. Improving the
environment

Name _____

Date _____

Improving Peddler's Park Junior School

Peddler's Park Junior School has been awarded a grant of £2000 to improve the school environment. Their headteacher, Mrs Outred, has asked each class to decide what they would most like to see improved around their school.

Show any working on the back of this sheet.

A 1 3A would like a set of football goals. If each goal costs £320 and each net costs £120, how much will a pair of each cost?

2 3B wants 2 basketball hoops for the playground. They cost £350 for the pair. How much does each one cost?

3 4A think that there are not enough trees in the school playground. If they buy 10 large trees at £54 each and 6 small trees at £10 each, how much would this cost altogether?

B 1 4B want to redecorate the library. They would like the walls painted and 4 new display boards erected. If the cost of the paint is £164 and each new display board £70, how much does it cost to redecorate the library?

2 4C want to build two more wheelchair access ramps in the school. If each ramp costs £670, how much will the two ramps cost?

3 5A would like to put 3 birdbaths in the school playground. If each birdbath costs £78, how much will this cost?

4 5B would like some markings painted on the playground. The paint costs £169.50 and the special machine they need to use costs £75 a day to hire, and they need it for 2 days. How much will this cost altogether?

C 1 5C want to build a school garden with flowers and vegetables. The materials needed to build the garden are £1042, the flowers £368 and the vegetables £144. How much is this altogether?

2 6A would like a pond area. The cost of the pond, plants and all other materials is £1328. The cost of the labour is £667. What is the total cost of the materials and labour?

3 6B want a higher fence put around the playground so they don't keep losing their ball. The cost of this is £1486. If the school decide to use the £2000 for this, how much change will they have?

Activity 17

Problems involving money
Geography: 18. Connecting
ourselves to the world

Name _____

Date _____

Quick-link Internet Company

Tariff	Conditions	Charge	Special Note
A	1 minute	1p	
B	1 month unlimited calls	£12.99 each month	
C	Up to 10 hours a month	£4.99 each month	Additional time charged at 1p a minute
D	Up to 20 hours a month	£8.99 each month	Additional time charged at 1p a minute
E	Up to 30 hours a month	£10.99 each month	Additional time charged at 1p a minute

Show any working on
the back of this sheet.

A 1 Joey is on Tariff A. This month he was on the internet for 2 hours. What will his bill be?

2 If Alice is on Tariff D, but only spends 9 hours a month on the internet, how much would she save each month by moving to Tariff C?

3 Martin is on Tariff A. Last month his bill was £6. How many hours was he on the internet for?

B 1 Sanjay is on Tariff D. Last month his bill was £9.37. How much longer than 20 hours did Sanjay spend on the internet?

2 Ashley is on Tariff C. Last month he spent 12 hours on the internet. What was his bill?

3 How much does Tariff C cost a year if you are on the internet for less than 10 hours each month?

4 Paul is on Tariff E. Last month he spent 30 hours and 47 minutes on the internet. What was his bill?

C 1 If James spends 1 hour a week on the internet, how much does it cost him over a year using Tariff A?

2 Earl is on the internet for 8 hours each month. Would he pay less on Tariff A or Tariff C? How much less each month?

3 Delroy is on Tariff D. On average he spends 25 hours a month on the internet. How much would he save each month by changing to Tariff E?

Activity 18

Problems involving money
Geography: 19. How and where
do we spend our time?

Name _____

Date _____

What we did last week

Show any working on the back of this sheet.

A 1 Dani goes for a swimming lesson each Wednesday. There are 3 other children in the class and each child pays £1.50. How much do they pay altogether?

2 On Monday Enid went to judo. This cost £1.60. On Thursday she went for her piano lesson which costs £12. How much did they cost altogether?

3 Juan goes to Spanish class every week. This costs £4.75 and he pays with a £5 note. How much change does he get?

B 1 Sally goes to a Maths Club once a week and it costs her Mum £4. If she goes to the club for 35 weeks in the year, how much does it cost her Mum for the year?

2 Lisa's Mum has paid £32 for her to have a tennis lesson each Monday for 10 weeks. How much does each lesson cost?

3 It costs Jake £3.75 each week for his basketball lesson and he has to pay 75p each way on the bus to get there and back. How much does it cost him altogether each week?

4 Every Thursday 27 children stay at school to play games. If each of them pays 50p, how much is this altogether?

C 1 Last week it was Samantha's 9th birthday and her Mum took her and 3 friends to the cinema. It cost £6.50 for Samantha and each of her friends and £10 for her Mum. How much change did her Mum get from £50?

2 There are 26 members in the school Chess Club. If they each pay 20p a week, how much does the Club make in a 12 week term?

3 Sanjay is learning the violin. It costs £120 to hire the violin for a year and his weekly lesson costs £12. If he has lessons for 40 weeks of the year, how much is this altogether?

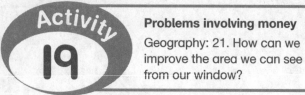

Activity 19

Problems involving money
Geography: 21. How can we improve the area we can see from our window?

Name _____

Date _____

Improving Moss Vale Primary

Moss Vale Primary School used to look out onto a park, but last year this was sold and a housing estate is being built on it. The school has therefore decided to create a nature area in the school playground.

> Show any working on the back of this sheet.

A 1 It costs £40 each day to hire a rubbish skip. The school needs to hire one for 5 days. How much does this cost?

2 The mechanical digger to dig the pond costs £200 to hire for $\frac{1}{2}$ a day. It also costs £80 to deliver it. How much is this altogether?

3 The plastic sheet to line the pond costs £10 for each square metre. If the pond needs a sheet of 30m², how much does this cost?

B 1 Rocks to go around the edge of the pond cost £127 and turf costs £108. How much do the rocks and turf cost altogether?

2 The school spends £276 on some shrubs and two small trees to go around the pond. The shrubs cost £142. The two trees cost the same amount each. How much do each of the trees cost?

3 Wooden fencing costs £12 for each metre length. If the nature area is 8 m by 10 m, how much would it cost for a fence around the perimeter?

4 A bird bath for the nature area costs £48.37 and a bird feeding table costs £24.85. What is the cost of these two items together?

C 1 The school spends £74.65 on water plants, fish and frogs for the pond. The water plants cost £57.35 and the fish cost £12.50. How much does each of the 3 frogs cost?

2 The school decides to buy a bench to commemorate the opening of the nature area. If the bench costs £267.45, the wood varnish £18.56, and the plaque £9.17, what is the total cost?

3 The school has a ceremony to open the nature area. The school secretary buys 8 bottles of drink at 93p each, tea, coffee and milk costing £4.53 and cakes and biscuits costing £9.16. If she pays with a £50 note, how much change does she receive?

Activity 20

Problems involving money
History: 9. What was it like for children in the Second World War?

Name _____

Date _____

Pay and costs during World War II

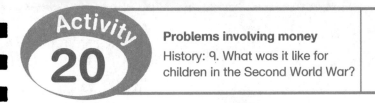

Weekly Pay in 1940		An average family's weekly expenses in 1940	
Unmarried soldier	£0.70	Rent	£0.53
Married soldier	£0.35	Coal	£0.22
Soldier's wife	£1.25	Gas and Electricity	£0.17
Female factory trainee	£1.90	Insurance	£0.23
Female factory worker	£4.50	Clothes	£0.15
Male factory trainee	£3.02	Food	£1.50
Male factory worker	£7.00	Other	£0.20

Show any working on the back of this sheet.

A 1 How much was a married soldier and his wife paid together each week?

2 How much more did an average family spend on rent than on insurance each week?

3 How much did an average family spend on rent and food altogether in a week?

B 1 What was the total of an average family's weekly expenses in 1940?

2 How much less a week was a female factory trainee paid than a male factory trainee?

3 How much more a week did a male factory trainee earn once he had finished his training and became a factory worker?

4 How much more did a male factory worker earn each week than a married soldier and his wife?

C 1 How much did a male factory worker earn in a 52 week year?

2 How much money did the average family need to live in a 52 week year?

3 What fraction of the weekly wage of a male factory worker did an unmarried soldier earn?

How long do they live?

This graph shows, in light grey, the average life span of different animals, including humans.
The black bar shows the additional life span of the longest living of these different types of animals.

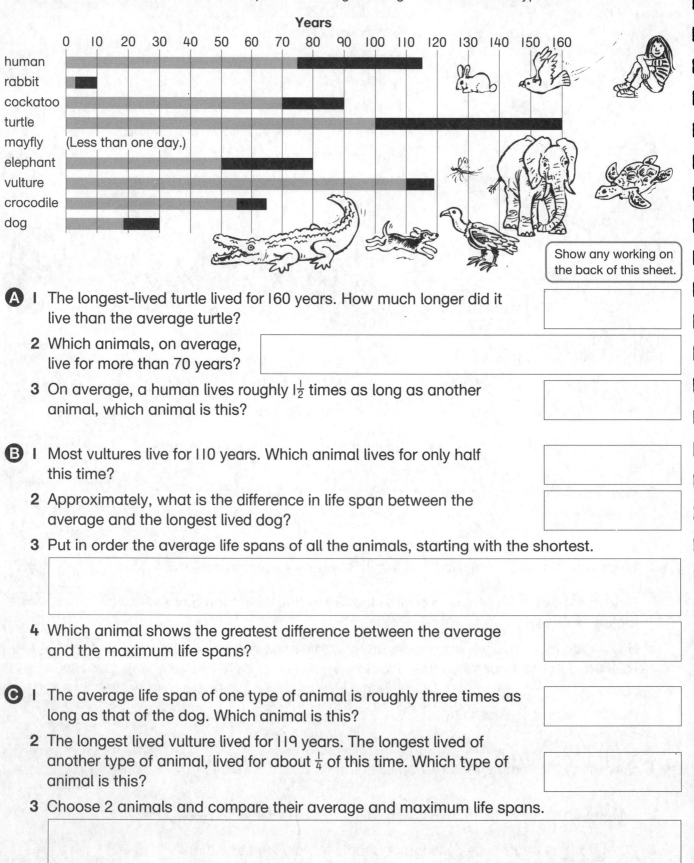

Years

Show any working on the back of this sheet.

A 1 The longest-lived turtle lived for 160 years. How much longer did it live than the average turtle?

2 Which animals, on average, live for more than 70 years?

3 On average, a human lives roughly $1\frac{1}{2}$ times as long as another animal, which animal is this?

B 1 Most vultures live for 110 years. Which animal lives for only half this time?

2 Approximately, what is the difference in life span between the average and the longest lived dog?

3 Put in order the average life spans of all the animals, starting with the shortest.

4 Which animal shows the greatest difference between the average and the maximum life spans?

C 1 The average life span of one type of animal is roughly three times as long as that of the dog. Which animal is this?

2 The longest lived vulture lived for 119 years. The longest lived of another type of animal, lived for about $\frac{1}{4}$ of this time. Which type of animal is this?

3 Choose 2 animals and compare their average and maximum life spans.

Thermometer readings

The pupils in 4L measured the temperature of different places and objects. The table shows their results.

Place/object	Temperature
Indoors	18° C
Outdoors	-2° C
Hot water from tap	59° C
Cold water from tap	7° C
Bowl of ice and water	0° C
Cup of tea	73° C
Boiling water	100° C
Drink from the fridge	2° C
Bag of frozen peas from the freezer	-16° C

Show any working on the back of this sheet.

A 1 How much hotter is the water from the hot tap than the cold tap?

2 What is the difference in temperature between the cup of tea and the boiling water?

3 The temperature of what place/object is 9 times greater than the temperature of the drink from the fridge?

B 1 What is the difference in temperature between indoors and outdoors?

2 How much cooler is the hot water from the tap than the cup of tea?

3 How much warmer is the drink from the fridge than the bag of frozen peas?

4 What is the difference in temperature between the hottest and the coldest place/object?

C 1 What is the difference in temperature between the bag of frozen peas and hot water from the tap?

2 The difference in temperature between outdoors and the bag of frozen peas is the same as the difference in temperature between two other places/objects. Which 2 other places/objects are these?

3 Write the temperatures in order, hottest to coldest.

Thermal insulators

Show any working on the back of this sheet.

A 1 500 ml of soup was poured into a thermos flask and 500 ml was poured into a bowl. After 15 minutes the temperature of the soup was 37° C in the bowl and 89° C in the thermos flask. How much cooler was the soup in the bowl?

2 A bag of ice takes 6 hours to melt in the insulated box. If it was left outside it would melt in 42 minutes. How much longer does it take to melt in the insulated box?

3 The Jones family go on a picnic. At 8:35 am they pack their cans of drink in an insulated box with ice. When they have their lunch at 1:00 pm the ice has still not melted. How long has it lasted?

B 1 Mrs. Edgedale is defrosting her freezer. She takes all the frozen food out and wraps it up together in a blanket to stop it from warming up. She starts at 2:05 pm and it takes her 75 minutes. At what time does she finish?

2 Mrs. Francis makes a pot of tea. If she puts a tea cosy on it, it takes 3 hr and 14 min to drop to room temperature. If she doesn't put the tea cosy on, it takes only 48 minutes. How much less time does it take without a cosy?

3 Year 4 pour 200 ml of boiling water into a thermos flask, 200 ml into a teapot with tea cosy and 200 ml into a teacup. After 20 min the temperature of the water in the teacup is 33° C. In the teapot it is 48° C more. What is the temperature in the teapot?

4 Mrs. White cooks a stew in the oven at 180° C. When it is cooked, she turns off the oven and leaves the stew inside. When she takes it out 1 hour later, the oven has only dropped 63° C. How hot is the oven now?

C 1 A thermos flask holds 1½ litres of coffee. How many 200 ml cups can this fill?

2 Tim sells ice creams on the beach from an insulated box. On a hot day, they stay frozen for 1 hr and 50 min. On a cooler day, they stay frozen for 40 minutes longer. For how long do they stay frozen when it is cooler?

3 At 9:45 am, Mrs. Dyas packs ice in a thermos flask for a picnic. She doesn't use it all, and discovers the remainder still frozen at 11:00 am the next day. For how long has it stayed frozen?

Problems involving measures
Science: 4D. Solids, liquids and
how they can be separated

Name _____

Date _____

The Bubbly Drinks Company

The Bubbly Drinks Company sells fizzy drinks.
They bottle their drinks in
different sized bottles
and cans.

2 litre bottle

$1\frac{1}{2}$ litre bottle

1 litre bottle

$\frac{1}{2}$ litre bottle

80 ml can

330 ml can

Show any working on the back of this sheet.

A 1 The Atar Restaurant wants to buy 50 litres of drink. How many 2 litre bottles do they buy?

2 How many $\frac{1}{2}$ litre bottles are the same as two 2 litre bottles?

3 Ahmed's mum buys three 2 litre bottles of drink for a picnic. The bottles are too big too fit into her picnic basket, so she pours the drink into empty $1\frac{1}{2}$ litre bottles instead. How many of these does she fill?

B 1 The 80 ml cans are packed in boxes of 6. How many millilitres does one box hold?

2 How many $\frac{1}{2}$ litre bottles contain the same amount of fizzy drink as two $1\frac{1}{2}$ litre bottles?

3 Mike's Diner sells one hundred 330 ml cans of drink each week. How many litres is this each week?

4 Sally is having a birthday party and her mum buys three $1\frac{1}{2}$ litre bottles and ten 330 ml cans. How much drink is this altogether?

C 1 Joe's Corner Store wants to buy 60 litres of drink, half of it in 2 litre bottles and the other half in $1\frac{1}{2}$ litre bottles. How many of each sized bottle do they buy?

2 The Bubbly Drinks Company sells their fizzy drink in 6 different sized bottles and cans. If you buy one of each of them, how many litres and millilitres is this altogether?

3 How many 80 ml cans contain the same amount of drink as one hundred 1 litre bottles?

The restaurant kitchen

Show any working on the back of this sheet.

(A) 1 Antonio is melting butter in a pan to make omelettes. The omelettes take 6 minutes to cook and he starts cooking them at 12:27 pm. At what time will they be cooked?

2 Jamie is making batter for pancakes. He sieves the flour to remove any lumps and then adds 400 ml of milk from a new 1 litre container. How much milk is left in the container?

3 Delia the pastry chef is making cakes. She mixes 240 g of flour with half this amount of sugar. How much flour and sugar is that altogether?

(B) 1 Rick is making pasta. He makes a roll 40 cm long and cuts it into pieces $2\frac{1}{2}$ cm long. How many pieces of pasta can he make from the 40 cm roll?

2 At 1:45 pm, Gordon places 5 litres of oil into the deep fat fryer to make chips, and turns it on. If it takes 16 minutes for the fryer to reach the right temperature, at what time can he put the chips in?

3 Rick makes stir-fry vegetables using equal weights of carrots, peas, beans, broccoli, bean sprouts and cabbage. If he wants to make 3 kg of stir-fry how much of each vegetable must he add?

4 The restaurant can serve 8 people from each kilogram of roast beef. How many kilograms and grams do they need to serve 50 people?

(C) 1 Nigella is making meringue. She whisks 4 dozen egg whites and then stirs in the sugar. If she has to add 660 g of sugar for every dozen eggs used, how much sugar must she add?

2 Gary is making jelly in a $7\frac{1}{2}$ litre mould. He dissolves 16 cubes of jelly for every $\frac{1}{2}$ litre of hot water used. How many cubes of jelly must he use?

3 Delia is making a chocolate cake using 640 g of flour and 320 g of sugar. For every 120 g of flour and sugar she has to add 8 spoonfuls of cocoa powder. How many spoonfuls of cocoa power must she add?

Parachutes

The pupils in 4E made parachutes out of different materials and in different sizes, to investigate which makes the best parachute. This table shows the flight times of the different parachutes.

Material	Size		
	20 cm x 20 cm	30 cm x 30 cm	40 cm x 40 cm
Writing paper	5·1 sec	7·5 sec	9·3 sec
Tissue paper	7·3 sec	14·7 sec	13·1 sec
Cotton	6·5 sec	10·8 sec	10·5 sec
Silk	8·7 sec	16·3 sec	15·4 sec

Show any working on the back of this sheet.

A 1 What is the difference in time between the longest flight and the shortest flight?

2 How many parachutes flew for longer than 10 seconds?

3 Which parachute flew roughly twice as long as the cotton 20 cm × 20 cm parachute?

B 1 What is the area of each of the 30 cm × 30 cm parachutes?

2 Which parachute flew 4·2 seconds longer than the cotton 40 cm × 40 cm parachute?

3 Of the 3 parachutes made from silk, one flew for 15·4 sec and another for 8·7 sec. What is this difference in flight time?

4 Which 3 parachutes flew the longest?

C 1 Place all the flight times in order, starting from the shortest.

2 Which parachute flew for roughly three times as long as the shortest flight?

3 Did the four 30 cm × 30 cm parachutes fly longer or shorter than the four 40 cm × 40 cm parachutes? How much longer or shorter?

Tobogganing

Show any working on the back of this sheet.

A 1 Alfred and Harry have a race down the hill. Harry reaches the bottom in 27 seconds and Alfred in 23 seconds. How much quicker is Alfred?

2 Lois and Delia don't own a toboggan so they use dinner trays instead. Lois takes 23 seconds. Delia gets stuck on a patch of grass and takes twice as long. How long does Delia take?

3 Ian and Vicki slide down together on their toboggan. They pass Zoe after 54 m and travel another 43 m. How far do they travel altogether?

B 1 Yolanda and Sylvester see who can go the furthest. Yolanda goes 214 m. Sylvester goes over a patch of grass and slows down. He goes 37 m less. How far does he go?

2 On his first try, Matthew gets stuck and only goes 57 m. On his second try he goes 134 m. How much further does he go on his second try?

3 Tommy takes 23 seconds to go down the slope and 4 minutes 15 seconds to climb up. How much longer does it take him to climb up the slope?

4 In the morning Yolanda goes 214 m down the hill. As the day goes on the sun melts some of the snow and in the afternoon the furthest she can go is 168 m. How much further does she travel in the morning?

C 1 Alfred has 4 goes at tobogganing down the slope. On the first go he travels 208 m, on the second 222 m, on the third 196 m, and on the fourth 158 m. What is the difference between his longest and his shortest goes?

2 Vicki arrives at the slopes at 10:30 am, and goes home for lunch at 12:50 pm. She then goes back for $1\frac{3}{4}$ hours in the afternoon. How long does she spend tobogganing altogether?

3 Overnight, about 27 mm of snow falls each hour for 7 hours. How much snow falls in the night?

Mr. and Mrs. Herne's farm

Show any working on the back of this sheet.

A 1 Mr. and Mrs. Herne live on a farm. Three times a week, Mrs. Herne travels 4 km into town to visit her mother and 4 km back. How many kilometres does she travel each week visiting her mother?

2 It is 4 km to drive from the Herne's farm into the village. There is a footpath which is only 3 km 250 m long. How much shorter is the footpath?

3 It only takes Mr. Herne 7 minutes to drive from the farm into the village. It takes him 55 minutes to walk from the farm into the village. How much quicker is it to drive?

B 1 Mr. Herne's mother lives 65 km away. When they go to visit her, they pick her up and take her to lunch in a restaurant 8 km further. After dropping her back, they return home. How many kilometres do they travel?

2 The postman travels 27 miles each day delivering mail. He does this 6 times a week. How many miles does he travel each week?

3 Once a week Mrs. Herne drives to the nearest large town. If the town is 9 miles away, how far does she drive to and from the town in a 4 week month?

4 Simon Herne works 26 km from home. If he works 5 days a week, how far does he travel each week to work and back?

C 1 Mr. and Mrs. Herne drive to London to see their daughter. They drive 4 km into the village and then another 18 km before they join the motorway. They stay on the motorway for 137 km and then it's a further 6 km to their daughter's house. How far away does their daughter live?

2 The mobile library visits the village once a week and stays for 3 hours. How many hours does it spend in the village in a 52 week year?

3 Mr. and Mrs. Herne's farm is 2·5 km long by 1·4 km wide. What is the area of their farm?

The village of Chembakolli

North
West ┼ East
South

Niligiri Hills
Road to other villages
Bathing tank
Well
Village Hall
Health centre
School
Temple
Main Road
Market
Police Station
To Gudalur
Post office
Temple
Cinema

Show any working on the back of this sheet.

A 1 Chembakolli is 300 km from Mysore but only 30 km from Gudalar, the nearest small town. How much closer is Chembakolli to Gudalar than Mysore?

2 What place lies to the west of the Health Centre?

3 If it is 190 metres to walk from a house in the village to the Bathing Tank, how far is it to walk there and back?

B 1 If you walk out of the Health Centre and travel east along the Main Road, what is the first place you come to on your right?

2 In which direction does the Well lie from the Bathing Tank?

3 To walk from a house in the village to the Well and back again is 300 m. If you do this 7 days a week, how far is this a week?

4 If you walk 327 m each way from your house to school and you go to school 5 days a week, how far do you walk to and from school each week?

C 1 It is 283 m from the School to the Temple on the Main Road, and 134 m from the Temple to the Cinema. How far is it from the School to the Cinema?

2 It is 365 m from the School to the Village Hall and 536 m from the School to the Bathing Tank. How far is it from the Village Hall to the Bathing Tank?

3 Apart from houses, which 2 buildings lie north west of the Cinema?

London, England and Sabah, Malaysia

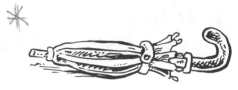

London, England

		J	F	M	A	M	J	J	A	S	O	N	D
Rainfall (mm)		52	40	35	36	47	45	55	57	49	54	65	48
Temperature	min	2	2	4	6	8	12	14	13	11	8	5	4
(°C)	max	6	7	10	12	17	20	22	21	19	14	10	7

Sabah, Malaysia

		J	F	M	A	M	J	J	A	S	O	N	D
Rainfall (mm)		245	107	142	262	467	600	523	512	628	694	607	483
Temperature	min	22	22	23	24	24·5	24	23·5	23·5	23·5	23·5	23	23
(°C)	max	29·5	30	30·5	31	31·5	31	30·5	30·5	30·25	30	30	30

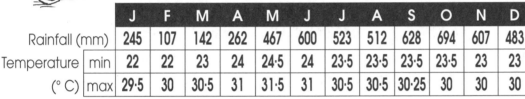

> Show any working on the back of this sheet.

A 1 How much more rain falls in London in July than in February?

2 In London, which month has the greatest difference between the minimum and maximum temperatures?

3 In Sabah, 107 mm of rain falls in February. In which month does 500 mm more than this fall?

B 1 How much more rain falls in June in Sabah than in London?

2 In Sabah, how many millimetres difference is there between the month with the most rainfall and the month with the least rainfall?

3 What is the total amount of rainfall in London in May, June, July and August?

4 How much rain falls altogether in the two wettest months of the year in Sabah?

C 1 In Sabah, which month has the greatest temperature range?

2 How much rain falls in London in a year?

3 In Sabah, seven months of the year have the same difference between the minimum and maximum temperatures. Which seven months are these?

Maths Facts (Y4) © HarperCollins*Publishers* Ltd 2003

Pond life

The pupils in Year 4 visited
the nature reserve
at Kiama.

> Show any working on
> the back of this sheet.

A 1 The children spotted two frogs living in the pond. If each frog lays 2300 eggs,
how many eggs are there altogether?

2 The children got to the pond at 10:25 am. They spent 1 hour and 10 min by
the pond before they had a break. At what time did they have their break?

3 There are 28 children in Year 4. To go pond dipping they were divided into
4 equal groups. How many children were in each group?

B 1 The children were divided into 4 groups and asked to count how many snails
they could find. One group counted 36 snails, another 45, another 27, and the
fourth group 18. How many snails did they count altogether?

2 The children counted 8 lily flowers. If there were 6 leaves for each flower, how
many lily leaves were there altogether?

3 A dragonfly has 4 wings. If the children counted 8 dragonflies, how many wings
did these dragonflies have altogether?

4 The pond was roughly rectangular in shape, and was 9 metres long by
7 metres wide. What was its area?

C 1 The children left the school at 8:20 am to travel to Kiama. They arrived
at 9:56 am. On the way back, they left at 3:05 pm and their journey
took 2 hours and 12 minutes. How long did they spend travelling
to and from Kiama altogether?

2 The cost of the visit to the Nature Reserve was £108.75 for the
children and £38.50 for the adults. What was the total cost for the
children and adults together?

3 The Park Ranger told the children that there are now 218 fish in the pond.
At the beginning of the year there were only 176. By how many have the
fish numbers increased?

Activity 32

Problems involving 'real life',
money and measures

Science: 4B. Habitats

Name _____

Date _____

Woodlands

The pupils in Year 4 visited
the nature reserve at Kiama.

Show any working on
the back of this sheet.

A 1 At 11:55 am the children went to the woodland. They were there until
1:05 pm. How long did they spend in the woodland?

2 Every 2 years, the trees in the woodland have to be thinned. How many times
have they been thinned in the last 40 years?

3 The children saw a nightingale in the wood. Nightingale eggs take 14 days to
hatch, and the chicks then spend 11 days in the nest. How many days is it
from when the eggs are laid till the chicks leave the nest?

B 1 Every 2 years, about 12 new trees are planted in the nature reserve. How many
trees have been planted in the past 10 years?

2 There are four families of foxes living in the wood. This year, one family had
5 cubs, 2 families had 4 cubs each and 1 family had 3 cubs. How many cubs
is this altogether?

3 In one clearing in the wood, the children counted 26 primroses and
17 foxgloves. How many flowers is this altogether?

4 There are 2 nature trails through the wood. The one that Year 4 took is
862 m long, the other one is 579 m long. How much longer is the one that
Year 4 took?

C 1 Year 4 entered the wood heading North, and came out of the wood
heading South. How many degrees of the compass difference is this?

2 In the shop at the nature reserve, Year 4 spent £18.65 altogether. If the
shop took £73.48 in total that day, how much did other people spend in
the shop that day?

3 The woodland is surrounded by a perimeter fence. If the woodland is
627 m long by 468 m wide, what is the distance of the perimeter?

The rabbit warren

Show any working on the back of this sheet.

A 1 Baby rabbits are called kits. They leave their burrow 3 weeks after birth. How many days do they spend in the burrow?

2 Kits are born blind and hairless. They grow hair after 8 days, and leave their burrow after 3 weeks. How many days after growing hair do they leave their burrow?

3 When a kit is born it weighs about 50 g. By the time it leaves its burrow, it weighs 150 g. By how much does it increase in weight in this time?

B 1 Each female rabbit has about 12 babies a year. If she has 3 babies at a time, how many times a year does she have babies?

2 The average running speed of a rabbit is 26 kilometres an hour. However, they can run as fast as 38 kilometres an hour. How much faster is this than the average?

3 6 rabbits eat as much grass as 1 sheep. If there are 72 rabbits in a warren, altogether they will eat as much grass as how many sheep?

4 A pair of rabbits can have 12 babies each year. After 1 year there are 14 rabbits and after 2 years there are 98 rabbits. By how many has the number of rabbits increased in the second year?

C 1 One warren of rabbits was recorded as having 407 rabbits and 2080 holes. If every rabbit had dug the same number of holes, approximately how many holes did each rabbit dig?

2 If the main tunnel in a warren is 17 m long and extending from this are 5 passages of 8 m each and 4 passages of 6 m each, what is the total length of all the passages?

3 If 12 rabbits each have 12 babies, how many rabbits altogether are there now?

Activity 34

Problems involving 'real life', money and measures
Geography: 8. Improving the environment

Name _____

Date _____

Recycling

The pupils in 4D have done a survey of the amount of recyclable waste the school produces in a week. The chart below shows their results.

PLEASE REUSE THIS BAG

	Paper	Glass bottles / jars	Aluminium cans	Tin cans	Plastic
Monday	15·3 kg	13	84	8	6·3 kg
Tuesday	21·7kg	26	76	12	5·3 kg
Wednesday	18·9 kg	31	69	9	8·1 kg
Thursday	24·1 kg	18	82	11	7 kg
Friday	26·3 kg	29	57	10	9·2 kg

> Show any working on the back of this sheet.

(A) 1 How many tin cans did the school collect for recycling during the week?

2 What was the combined weight of paper and plastic that the school collected on Monday?

3 Which day of the week did the school collect the most paper and plastic?

(B) 1 What was the total number of glass bottles and jars collected by the school for recycling during the week?

2 The school gets $1\frac{1}{2}$ pence for every empty aluminium can they recycle. How much money did they get back from aluminium cans on Monday?

3 How many more aluminium cans did the school collect on Monday than Friday?

4 What is the total weight of plastic that the school collected over the week?

(C) 1 What was the total amount of paper collected by the school for recycling during the week, rounded to the nearest kilogram?

2 The school receives 47p for each computer printer cartridge they recycle. If they recycle 6 cartridges on average each month, how much do they make each month?

3 If the school makes roughly £27 each month from recycling, how much do they make in the nine months of the school year?

The village of Wellford

Show any working on the back of this sheet.

A 1 Frog River runs through Wellford. For most of the distance it is 80 cm deep. At one place, where there used to be a ford, the river is only 15 cm deep. How much shallower is the river here?

2 The bus fare from Wellford to the nearest large town is £1.45 each way. How much does it cost to go there and back?

3 Today, the population of Wellford is 178. Of these, 23 work in the village and 49 work in the surrounding area. How many more people work in the surrounding area than in the village?

B 1 The railway bridge over the High Street in Wellford is 3·5 metres above the road level. There is a gap of only 14 cm between the top of Mr. Tyler's truck and the bottom of the bridge. How high is Mr. Tyler's truck?

2 In the eighteenth century, Wellford had a population of 247. Today it has only 178 people. How many fewer people live in Wellford today?

3 There are 2 trains a day from Wellford. The first leaves at 8:16 am and the second leaves at 2:34 pm. How long after the morning train is the afternoon train?

4 The train from Wellford to the nearest large town takes 46 minutes. The bus takes 1 hour 23 minutes. How much longer does the bus take?

C 1 20 years ago, Walnut Cottage sold for £12 000. Last year it sold for £81 000. By how much has its value increased?

2 There is no longer a Post Office in the village. The postman now comes from the nearest large town, which is 54 km there and back. If he does this 6 times a week, how many kilometres does he travel in a week?

3 The Laughing Fox pub is open from 10:00 am till 2:30 pm and then from 5:00 pm till 11:00 pm Monday to Friday. On Saturday it is open from 10:30 am till 11:00 pm and on Sunday from 10:30 am till 10:30 pm. For how many hours is it open each week?

Padmi, a woman from Chembakolli

Show any working on the back of this sheet.

A 1 Every day Padmi carries home 10 litres of water from the well on her head. How much water does she carry home in a 7 day week?

2 The well is 160 m from Padmi's home. How far does she walk to the well and back?

3 Padmi starts working in the tea fields at 10:30 am and works for $4\frac{1}{2}$ hours. At what time does she finish?

B 1 Every day Padmi collects 20 kg of wood from the forest, which she carries home for cooking. How much wood does she carry home in a 7 day week?

2 Padmi works $4\frac{1}{2}$ hours a day in the tea fields. If she works in the fields 6 days a week, how many hours is this a week?

3 Padmi wakes up at 5:00 am every morning and goes to bed at 8:30 pm. How long is her day?

4 The tea field where Padmi works is 300 m from her house. If she works 6 days a week, how far does she walk to the tea fields and back each week?

C 1 Padmi's sister lives 12 km away. If she visits her 6 times a year, how far does she walk there and back in a year?

2 When Padmi is away from the house, her eldest daughter Chada, looks after the younger children. Padmi spends $\frac{1}{2}$ hr at the well and 1 hr collecting wood, 7 days a week and $4\frac{1}{2}$ hours working in the fields, 6 days a week. How many hours a week does Chada look after the other children?

3 Padmi has 26 male relatives and 17 female relatives. Her husband has 19 male relatives and 22 female relatives. How many more relatives does Padmi have than her husband?

Activity 37

Problems involving 'real life' and measures
Geography: 16. What's in the news?

Name _____

Date _____

Briton in Spacewalk

The Daily Voice

Piers Sellers has become only the third Briton to go into space, and only the second to carry out a space walk. The 47-year-old was part of the six man crew of the Space Shuttle Atlantis which blasted off from Florida on Monday 7th October 2002 at 8:45pm.

The Shuttle is on an 11 day mission to bring a giant girder and fresh food to the International Space Station. The two spacecraft linked up 240 miles above central Asia, and will remain docked together for 7 days.

Sellers is making 3 spacewalks to help fit the 45 ft long, 15 ft wide girder to the Space Station. The girder, which weighs 14 tonnes, brings the weight of the Space Station to 166 tonnes.

All parts for the Space Station have been taken into space by 15 American Space Shuttle flights and 15 Russian rocket flights. The parts have been attached together during 25 spacewalks from Space Shuttles and 21 spacewalks from the Space Station itself – a total of 285 hours and 25 minutes of spacewalks.

The 3 man crew of the Space Station are the 5th crew to man the Station, and have been in space for 4 months now, carrying out 25 scientific experiments.

**by our Space Correspondent
Sunny Star**

Show any working on the back of this sheet.

A **1** The Space Shuttle took off from Florida on 7th October. The mission lasted 11 days. What date did the Space Shuttle land back on Earth?

2 The Shuttle's mission lasted 11 days. For 7 of these days it was docked with the International Space Station. For how many days was it not docked with the Space Station?

3 So far, there have been 15 American flights to the Space Station and the same number of Russian flights. How many flights in total have there been?

B **1** So far, there have been 25 spacewalks from Space Shuttles and 21 spacewalks from the Space Station itself. How many spacewalks is this?

2 The Space Shuttle attached a 14 tonne girder to the Space Station. This made the total weight of the Space Station 166 tonnes. What was the weight of the Space Station before the girder was attached?

3 There have been 5 different crews living on the Space Station. The longest stay has been 196 days and the shortest 131 days. How many days difference is this?

4 So far, the crews of the Space Station have eaten 6000 meals and 4000 snacks. How many meals and snacks is this altogether?

C **1** The girder that the Space Shuttle was carrying was 45 foot long, and its width was one third of this. How wide was the girder?

2 The 5 crews that have lived on the Space Station have each needed 2·7 tonnes of supplies. How many tonnes of supplies is this in total?

3 The first Space Station crew lived there for 139 days, the second for 167 days, the third for 131 days, the fourth for 196 days and the fifth for 134 days so far. How many days is this altogether?

Elroy's week

The pupils in 4L were asked to keep a record of what they did last week. This is what Elroy did.

Show any working on the back of this sheet.

(A) 1 Elroy takes the bus to and from school each day. It costs him 50p each way. How much did it cost him for the 5 days last week?

2 On 4 days last week Elroy watched TV for 2 hr each day. On Friday he watched for $3\frac{1}{2}$ hr. On Saturday and Sunday he watched for 4 hr each day. How long did he spend watching TV last week?

3 Last week Elroy's maths lessons lasted for 50 min, 45 min, 1 hr, 1 hr and 50 min. How long did he spend doing maths last week?

(B) 1 Elroy spent $6\frac{1}{2}$ hours at school each day for 5 days. How many hours did he spend at school?

2 Each school day, Elroy had 20 minutes for his morning break and 1 hr for his lunch break. How long did he have for breaks during the 5 school days?

3 Last week Elroy spent 45 min on PE and 1 hr on sport at school. He also played football for $1\frac{1}{2}$ hr on Saturday and went swimming for 40 min on Sunday. Altogether how long was this?

4 Elroy goes for a swimming lesson each Sunday for 38 weeks of the year. If each lesson costs £1.50, how much does this cost in a year?

(C) 1 Last week from Sunday night to Thursday night, Elroy went to bed at 8:30 pm and got up at 7:00 am. On Friday and Saturday night he went to bed at 10:00 pm and got up at 8:30 am. How long did he spend in bed last week?

2 Elroy buys his lunch at the canteen at school. On Monday he spent £1.45, on Tuesday £1.32, on Wednesday and Thursday £1.68 each day, and on Friday £1.56. How much did he spend last week on lunch?

3 There are 168 hr in a week. If Elroy spent 42 hr at school and doing homework and 70 hr sleeping, how many hours did he spend doing other things?

Activity 39

Problems involving 'real life', money and measures

History: 9. What was it like for children in the Second World War?

Name _____

Date _____

Rationing in World War II

During World War II food was in short supply and was rationed in both Britain and Germany.

Food rations for 1 person in Britain each week

115 g bacon or ham
6p worth of meat
250 g fat, including butter
30 g cheese
1·8 litres milk
225 g sugar
50 g jam
55 g tea
1 egg
88 g sweets

Food rations for 1 person in Germany each week

450 g meat
2·2 kg bread
340 g fat, including butter
340 g sugar
453 g coffee

> Show any working on the back of this sheet.

A 1 How much fat and sugar altogether was each German allowed a week?

2 How much money was a British family of 5 allowed to spend each week on meat?

3 How many eggs were a man and his wife allowed together each year in Britain?

B 1 How much more fat was a German allowed each week than a Briton?

2 How much less sugar was a Briton allowed than a German each week?

3 How many grams of sweets was a child allowed in Britain each fortnight?

4 If a British person used 50 g of sugar to make a cake one week, how much sugar did she have left?

C 1 How many loaves of bread each weighing 440 g could a German have each week during the war?

2 During the war a British family of 5 people spent £1.50 on food each week. If each person spent 6p a week on meat, how much did the family spend on the rest of their food?

3 How many litres of milk was a family of 4 allowed each week in Britain?

Brian's Life

Show any working on the back of this sheet.

A 1 Brian was born in Africa in 1956. He moved to England with his mum, dad and older sister when he was 5. In what year did he move to England?

2 From the age of 7, Brian was given 5p a week pocket money. With this he could buy 100 g of sweets. How much did 1 kg of sweets cost?

3 When Brian was 8 years old his parents went to live in Hong Kong and he went to boarding school. He was given £1 pocket money each term. If he spent 17p on a model aeroplane kit, how much did he have left that term?

B 1 Brian only saw his parents for 8 weeks a year during the summer holidays. How many weeks a year did he not see his parents?

2 When Brian flew to Hong Kong the journey took 24 hours there and 24 hours back. If Brian had 8 weeks holiday, what fraction of his holiday did he spend travelling to Hong Kong and back?

3 In Hong Kong Brian's parents lived on the 12th floor of an apartment block. If the block had 20 floors with 2 apartments on each floor, what fraction of the apartments were above Brian's parents?

4 When Brian was 11 years old, his pocket money was increased to £2.50 a term. If there were 10 weeks in the term and Brian spent the same amount of money each week, how much money did he have to spend each week?

C 1 At school Brian played sport three afternoons a week. The playing fields were $3\frac{1}{2}$ miles from the school. How many miles did Brian travel to the playing fields and back each week?

2 When Brian was at boarding school he would spend every Sunday afternoon at a friend's house. He would arrive at 12:15 pm and leave at 4:45 pm. How many hours altogether did Brian spend there in a 10 week term?

3 Brian went to boarding school for 10 years altogether. If he spent 36 weeks each year at school, how many weeks did he not spend at school during this time?

Answers

Activity 1
What do you eat?

A 1 3–5 years
  2 470
  3 1–2 years

B 1 570
  2 280
  3 730
  4 250

C 1 464
  2 1194
  3 65 calories less

Activity 2
Bones and things

A 1 21
  2 24
  3 5

B 1 94
  2 103
  3 6 kg
  4 8·5 cm

C 1 2 years 215 days or 945 days
  2 $\frac{9}{20}$
  3 10 kg

Activity 3
The Six o'clock News

A 1 45
  2 62
  3 1 hr 20 min

B 1 36
  2 8
  3 2000
  4 48

C 1 55
  2 915
  3 11 100

Activity 4
The Roman navy and army

A 1 420
  2 12 km
  3 100 denarii

B 1 90 km
  2 4 hours
  3 4·2 m
  4 3

C 1 420
  2 35
  3 15

Activity 5
The Saxons

A 1 26 years
  2 12
  3 24

B 1 120
  2 £1.04
  3 1000 shillings
  4 108

C 1 10 000 m²
  2 24
  3 1650

Activity 6
The Vikings

A 1 70
  2 12 metres
  3 11:00 pm

B 1 8
  2 220 cm or 2 m 20 cm or 2·2 m
  3 386 km
  4 4800 km

C 1 9 m × 9 m
  2 $\frac{1}{5}$
  3 150 km

Activity 7
Henry VIII

A 1 7 years
  2 7 years
  3 10 years old

B 1 24 years
  2 29 years old
  3 26 years
  4 52 years old

C 1 17 years
  2 Catherine of Aragon, 24 years
  3 7 years

Activity 8
Rich and poor Tudors

A 1 69 years
  2 700
  3 4 hours

B 1 $10\frac{1}{2}$ hours
  2 720
  3 25
  4 540

C 1 13 600
  2 £2.50
  3 50

Activity 9
Tutankhamun's Tomb

A 1 22 years
  2 23rd November 1922
  3 16 m²

B 1 2600
  2 473
  3 48
  4 465

C 1 2900–3000 hours
  2 48 years old
  3 1346 BC

Activity 10
Ancient Egypt

A 1 1000
  2 20
  3 2400

B 1 48 days
  2 920 m
  3 March
  4 500

C 1 810
  2 6530 km
  3 20

Activity 11
The cost of keeping warm

A 1 £72
  2 Electric blanket
  3 32p

B 1 £68
  2 £1.60
  3 £327
  4 £753

C 1 £1800
  2 £216
  3 11

Activity 12
Sandy's Fish and Chip Shop

A 1 £3.30
  2 £1.45
  3 £1

B 1 £5.45
  2 £18
  3 £48
  4 £11.80

C 1 £15
  2 £3.77
  3 £575.80

Activity 13
The Better Electrics' Sale

A 1 £25
  2 £25.99
  3 £3.96

B 1 £614
  2 Game station
  3 £183
  4 £330

C 1 Desktop computer
  2 £35
  3 £205.92

Activity 14
Sparky the electrician

A 1 £260
  2 £147.50
  3 £520

B 1 £24.50
  2 £45
  3 £85
  4 £1300

C 1 £117.06
  2 £1300
  3 £1142

Activity 15
The electrician's shop

A 1 £3.90 a metre
  2 50p
  3 £28.20

B 1 £10.50
  2 £130
  3 £1
  4 £3.30

C 1 £22
  2 £33.40
  3 £312

Activity 16
Improving Peddler's Park Junior School

A 1 £880
  2 £175
  3 £600

B 1 £444
  2 £1340
  3 £234
  4 £319.50

C 1 £1554
  2 £1995
  3 £514

Activity 17
Quick-link Internet Company

A 1 £1.20
  2 £4
  3 10 hours

B 1 38 min
  2 £6.19
  3 £59.88
  4 £11.46

C 1 £31.20
  2 Tariff A/19p
  3 £1

Activity 18
What we did last week

A 1 £6
  2 £13.60
  3 25p

B 1 £140
  2 £3.20
  3 £5.25
  4 £13.50

C 1 £14
  2 £62.40
  3 £600

Activity 19
Improving Moss Vale Primary

A 1 £200
   2 £280
   3 £300

B 1 £235
   2 £67
   3 £432
   4 £73.22

C 1 £1.60
   2 £295.18
   3 £28.87

Activity 20
Pay and costs during World War II

A 1 £1.60
   2 £0.30
   3 £2.03

B 1 £3
   2 £1.12
   3 £3.98
   4 £5.40

C 1 £364
   2 £156
   3 $\frac{1}{10}$

Activity 21
How long do they live?

A 1 60 years
   2 humans, turtles and vultures
   3 elephant

B 1 crocodile
   2 11 years or 12 years
   3 less than 1 day, 3 years, 18 years, 50 years, 55 years, 70 years, 75 years, 100 years, 110 years
   4 turtle

C 1 crocodile
   2 dog
   3 e.g. The average life span of a human is 75 years, but the average life span of a cockatoo is 5 years less. The longest lived human lived for about 25 years longer than the longest lived cockatoo.

Activity 22
Thermometer readings

A 1 52° C
   2 27° C
   3 indoors

B 1 20° C
   2 14° C
   3 18° C
   4 116° C

C 1 75° C
   2 cup of tea and hot water from the tap
   3 100° C, 73° C, 59° C, 18° C, 7° C, 2° C, 0° C, –2° C, –16° C

Activity 23
Thermal insulators

A 1 52° C
   2 5 hr 18 min
   3 4 hr 25 min

B 1 3:20 pm
   2 2 hr 26 min
   3 81° C
   4 117° C

C 1 7 or $7\frac{1}{2}$
   2 2 hr 30 min
   3 25 hr 15 min

Activity 24
The Bubbly Drinks Company

A 1 25
   2 8
   3 4

B 1 480 ml
   2 6
   3 33 litres
   4 7800 ml or 7 l 800 ml or 7.8 l

C 1 2 litre – 15; 1½ litre – 20
   2 5 l 410 ml
   3 1250

Activity 25
The restaurant kitchen

A 1 12:33 pm
   2 600 ml
   3 360 g

B 1 16
   2 2:01 pm
   3 $\frac{1}{2}$ kg or 500 g
   4 6 kg 250 g or $6\frac{1}{4}$ kg

C 1 2640 g or 2 kg 640 g
   2 240
   3 64

Activity 26
Parachutes

A 1 11·2 sec
   2 6
   3 Tissue paper, 40 cm × 40 cm

B 1 900 cm²
   2 Tissue paper, 30 cm × 30 cm
   3 6·7 sec
   4 Silk, 30 cm × 30 cm; Silk, 40 cm × 40 cm; Tissue paper 30 cm × 30 cm

C 1 5·1 sec; 6·5 sec;
7·3 sec; 7·5 sec;
8·7 sec; 9·3 sec;
10·5 sec; 10·8 sec;
13·1 sec; 14·7 sec;
15·4 sec; 16·3 sec
2 Silk, 40 × 40 cm
3 Longer/1 sec

Activity 27
Tobogganing

A 1 4 sec
2 46 sec
3 97 m

B 1 177 m
2 77 m
3 3 min 52 sec
4 46 m

C 1 64 m
2 4 hr 5 min
3 189 mm or
18 cm 9 mm or
18·9 cm

Activity 28
Mr. and Mrs. Herne's Farm

A 1 24 km
2 750 m
3 48 min

B 1 146 km
2 162 miles
3 72 miles
4 260 km

C 1 165 km
2 156 hours
3 3·5 km²

Activity 29
The village of Chembakolli

A 1 270 km
2 School
3 380 metres

B 1 Temple
2 West
3 2100 m or
2 km 100 m or 2·1 km
4 3270 m or 3 km 270 m
or 3·27 km

C 1 417 m
2 171 m
3 Temple and Village Hall

Activity 30
London, England and Sabah, Malaysia

A 1 15 mm
2 May
3 November

B 1 555 mm
2 587 mm
3 204 mm
4 1322 mm

C 1 February
2 583 mm
3 A, M, J, J, A, N, D

Activity 31
Pond life

A 1 4600
2 11:35 am
3 7

B 1 126
2 48
3 32
4 63 m²

C 1 3 hr 48 min
2 £147.25
3 42

Activity 32
Woodlands

A 1 1 hr 10 min
2 20
3 25 days

B 1 60
2 16
3 43
4 283 m

C 1 180°
2 £54.83
3 2190 m

Activity 33
The rabbit warren

A 1 21 days
2 13 days
3 100 g

B 1 4
2 12 kilometres an hour
3 12
4 84

C 1 5
2 81 m
3 156

Activity 34
Recycling

A 1 50
2 21·6 kg
3 Friday

B 1 117
2 £1.26
3 27
4 35·9 kg

C 1 106 kg
2 £2.82
3 £243

Activity 35
The village of Wellford

A 1 65 cm
    2 £2.90
    3 26

B 1 3 m 36 cm or 336 cm
    2 69
    3 6 hr 18 min
    4 37 min

C 1 £69 000
    2 324 km
    3 77 hours

Activity 36
Padmi, a woman from Chembakolli

A 1 70 litres
    2 320 m
    3 3:00 pm

B 1 140 kg
    2 27 hours
    3 $15\frac{1}{2}$ hours
    4 3600 m or 3 km 600 m or 3·6 km

C 1 144 km
    2 $37\frac{1}{2}$ hours
    3 2

Activity 37
Briton in Spacewalk

A 1 18th October
    2 4 days
    3 30

B 1 46
    2 152 tonnes
    3 65 days
    4 10 000

C 1 15 foot
    2 13·5 tonnes
    3 767 days

Activity 38
Elroy's week

A 1 £5
    2 $19\frac{1}{2}$ hr
    3 4 hr 25 min

B 1 $32\frac{1}{2}$ hours
    2 6 hr 40 min
    3 3 hr 55 min
    4 £57

C 1 $73\frac{1}{2}$ hr
    2 £7.69
    3 56 hr

Activity 39
Rationing in World War II

A 1 680 g
    2 30p
    3 104

B 1 90 g
    2 115 g
    3 176 g
    4 175 g

C 1 5
    2 £1.20
    3 7 l 200 ml or 7·2 litres

Activity 40
Brian's life

A 1 1961
    2 50p
    3 83p

B 1 44 weeks
    2 $\frac{2}{56}$ or $\frac{1}{28}$
    3 $\frac{8}{20}$, $\frac{4}{10}$ or $\frac{2}{5}$
    4 25p

C 1 21 miles
    2 45 hours
    3 160 weeks